For permission requests, mail the publisher via YourTimePublishing@gmail.com

TABLE OF CONTENTS

LIVE

In memory of my family, friends, and mentors
who, from beyond their graves, still find ways
to help, motivate, and encourage me.

INTRODUCTION

"Stress should be a powerful driving force, not an obstacle."(Bill Phillips)

This is the first of a tetralogy -- a four book series -- focused on helping you realize that, if what you are doing at any given point in time is not "Living, Loving, Laughing, or Learning" to the best of your abilities, then something is amiss.

Over the years, several misconceptions have trailed the concept, understanding, and use of the term "stress". Many people equate it with pressure or overwork, and many believe it is a key indicator of anxiety, grief, illness, or fear. To a large degree, stress is associated with unfavorable circumstances and everyone is encouraged to avoid it. The typical dictionary associates stress with pressure, force, worry, or uncomfortable feelings. Several scientists, social psychologists, and physicians have also seconded this perspective (Das 2022). Stress is blamed as the culprit when you feel bad, stuck, injured, or uncertain, and is pinpointed as a source of a wide range of unwanted habits. This large momentum of negativity attached to the word "stress" made me wonder: is anything positive about stress?

The short answer is yes! We may have adopted a parochial

approach all along. But stress has a lot of positives. Unless you "stress", you cannot break certain unwanted habits or accomplish new feats. You cannot easily increase your alertness and performance. Your body's growth will be limited without stress. Your immune system will not be optimized without stress. The fact is that stress is one of the healthy, positive, and important psychological responses the human body elicits on the path to creativity. You only have to work towards the right stress -- the good stress, or eustress. This realization may conjure some questions, such as:

- What is eustress?
- What are examples of these good stresses?
- How do you *Fix Yourself and LIVE the Happy Path by Using 9 Eustress Exercises to Transform, Change Habits, and Find Balance*?

If you are reading this book, you are likely seeking answers to questions like these and more. You probably want to know how stress can be beneficial to you, and to learn some practical ways to help you better yourself.

What you have in your hand is a detailed book of explanations, theories, solutions, and recommendations that I have researched and tried myself to help realize, understand, learn, and appreciate. My goal is to guide you to see the value of using stress for the development and fine-tuning of your mind and body in your personal and professional life.

This is not a consolidation of Western facts. It is a collection from several average people, some professionals, and myself, who have broken new ground as a result of excellent stress and body management techniques. You are in for a fulfilling journey to challenge unwanted habits and overcome perceived limitations using proven principles. Brace yourself for interesting discoveries, and set aside time to reeducate yourself -- well -- on yourself.

Here, I aim to help you break through stagnant, confining barriers that often make you feel like you cannot reach your full potential. I want to help you figure out why you feel like you are limited. You will be given tools to help you learn how to push beyond your limits through good stress -- eustress -- and ensure that your body and soul are catered for. Our unwanted habits and perceived limitations mostly originate from our history, choices, actions, and inactions. The simple things you do every day, the complex ones, and the ease with which you can switch to healthier habits contribute to your overall success.

The spectrum of severity of unwanted habits or perceived limitations can vary greatly from one person to the next. What might seem simple to one might be devastating to another. So try not to over- or underestimate your concerns or those of others. Regardless of whether you are, for example, trying to stop chewing with your mouth open, trying to quit smoking, being forever in a rush and always late, or always thinking that you are not enough, you have the ability to change, improve, and *Fix Yourself*. With this book, you can find help to healthier alternatives and discover how to gradually transition with confidence.

Extreme unwanted habits might include clinical diseases like alcoholism, drug abuse, clinical depression, and many others. This book will focus more on unwanted habits and perceived limitations that are considered non-clinical issues. As such, this is not a substitute for a medical professional. Rather, it is a lifetime compilation of unwanted habit- and limitation-breaking theories that have been personally learned, researched, practiced, and refined.

As you discover and identify your own unwanted habits, perceived limitations, and healthier alternatives, you should implement change, but implement it slowly. Do not try to shock your body to the extent that it causes harm. The late South African Bishop Desmond Tutu said, "There is only one way to eat an elephant: a bite at a time." It took a lifetime to develop your unwanted habits, so it will take work to correct them. But, if you are willing to do the work to change these undesired habits, you can. And you will -- one bite at a time.

Before you can take the first "bite of your elephant", you must identify which unwanted habits or perceived limitations you have. This is typically not too difficult since you have noticed them yourself or have been alerted to them by someone else. The desire for self-improvement is likely one of the reasons why you are reading this book.

A more difficult task is to determine what triggers your unwanted habits. This might be harder to notice because it requires paying attention and admitting to the trigger-to-habit relationship. Harder still might be determining the source or origin of the trigger itself. The theory on this relationship is discussed in the chapters ahead.

To accomplish any of these do-it-yourself practices, you must start by calming yourself. Relax. Love and forgive yourself before even beginning to think of fixing, changing, or healing yourself. Set yourself up for success by welcoming change, and be open to introducing new, controlled, healthy stress -- eustress -- to help you combat your unwanted habits and plateaus.

You will find improved self-confidence to break your unwanted habits and break through your perceived limitations if you take the time to read and regularly practice the eustress activities offered in this book.

Be sure to read between the lines to determine how each situation can be applied to your unique situation. This book is your game-changer if you are open to new ideas and concepts that will help you to *Fix Yourself.*

Who am I?

I am an average person like you. I have a family, job, responsibilities, hurts, pains, stress, faults, hopes, dreams, and goals -- just like you. But I have come to understand that in the game of life, the human mind is a powerful connector that can be hacked by the owner if the owner chooses to.

If you allow negative stress and other life circumstances to affect you, you will always feel lost, down, depressed, and insufficient. You need to snap out of it, and take control of your mind, body, and soul. Knowing this is one thing. But having the confidence to brave the fear of change may need some encouragement, support, and tools to assist you.

This book constitutes a lifetime collection of concepts resulting from my own curiosity and drive to educate myself on how to break through the feeling of being limited. I was particularly intrigued because several people who have achieved balance in their personal life, relationships, and businesses have adopted some of these skills. Using these learned skills has helped me feel unstoppable.

How to use this book

Every chapter in this book is important if your ambition is to *Fix Yourself*. However, if you are already familiar with eustress, the habit cycle, the importance of sleep and rest, the importance of balance in your life, and are aware that your body changes with age and how to compensate, then feel free to skip to Chapter 7, where we dive into hands-on methods and exercises for applying eustress that you can start today. By the conclusion, you should feel inspired and capable of stepping out of the comfort zones that you have known for a lifetime. You will want to change the reactions to your triggers, and you will consciously and repeatedly look to introduce eustress -- the good stress.

Quite possibly, the most powerful and important of the nine eustresses to apply can be found in Chapter 14. But careful consideration was put into the order of the chapters due to the manner in which they can support and build upon each other. So it is best to read from Chapter 1 through to Chapter 15, all in sequence.

Let us begin.

CHAPTER 1

OVERVIEW OF THE THEORY OF STRESS

"It is not stress that kills us, it is our reaction to it."
(Hans Selye)

The theory of stress has been around for centuries, with different people proposing different ideas about what it is and how it works. To begin, I will give a brief overview of some types of stress and their various places in our lives. Then, we will go on to understand how stress leads you to develop new habits and how to identify what unwanted habit needs to be fixed.

Types of stress

Acute stress: Physical stress can lead to major injuries, broken bones, and more obvious physical results. On the mental side, acute stress can be caused by things like deadlines, public speaking, or a fight with a loved one. These stresses are often short-lived as they can have closure. A broken bone will heal. A presentation will conclude. You can make up after the fight.

Chronic stress: Emotional stress is more typically associated with stress where we use terms like "being stressed out". This could be a response to a perceived threat, danger, or fear such as losing your job, moving your residence, the death of someone you care about, a relationship breakup, work overload, and so on. The symptoms of chronic stress are often mental, such as anxiety, depression, or irritability. These types of stress are often longer term as they are often based on worry or other types of fear.

Traumatic stress: However, stresses do not need to be current. Historical events like childhood experiences -- either emotional or physical -- can continue to affect you today. This type of stress can be caused by a traumatic event that may even be related to an acute or chronic stress such as a car accident, a death in the family, or a natural disaster. A generalized example of traumatic stress is better known as post-traumatic stress disorder (PTSD). The symptoms of traumatic stress can be both physical and mental, and they can last for months, years, or a lifetime if left unchecked.

When triggered, the symptoms of acute, chronic, and traumatic stresses are often physical, even if it is an emotional stress. Cardinal Lamberto (*The Godfather*) quite accurately stated, "when the mind suffers, the body cries out".

What may present itself in a minor way at first, such as a racing heart, sweaty palms, and tense muscles, is the body reacting to stress by activating the nervous system and releasing a cocktail of chemical messengers. These chemicals are neurotransmitters that are attempting to protect our bodies by preparing them for potential physical activity of some sort by increasing heart rate, blood pressure, blood sugar, and many other possible things, measurable or not. Most likely, many nerotransmitters have not even been discovered yet -- let alone their effects.

Picture yourself in any traumatic situation, let alone several at once, and you will likely experience some of these symptoms just through your own imagination as you sit reading this book. These symptoms are normal, expected, and are used by our bodies in an attempt to protect us. But when stresses are repetitive, combined, and not dealt with, dangerous levels of negative physical manifestation can be reached, which can lead to scarring effects on our minds and bodies.

Eustress: The implications of stress, however, can be both positive and negative. For example, it can be motivating to meet a deadline and achieve a goal. Without the stress of being exposed to diseases, our immune systems would not develop properly. Without using our muscles, they would atrophy and become vestigial.

In the mid-1930s, the Hungarian endocrinologist Hans Selye coined the term "eustress" to differentiate good stress from acute, chronic, and traumatic negative stresses, which he categorized as "distress". Eustress is derived from the Greek prefix "eu-", meaning good, and "stress", meaning pressure. We should all experience and seek out eustress and avoid distress. However, avoiding distress entirely is unlikely in our lifetimes.

When we are stressed, our bodies prepare to fight or flee by releasing neurotransmitters and hormones like adrenaline and cortisol. And everybody will react a little (or a lot) differently to different stresses based on their own personal history. This applies to both distress and eustress.

Both eustress and distress can originate from the same source. It depends on the person, the place they are at in their lives, what happened to them that day, what happened to them in the past, and countless other factors. In the workplace, being selected to publicly present to a group of people might be eustress to one person who sees it as an opportunity to shine. But it may be distress to an introvert who does not like people looking at them. Various and selected eustresses can lead to increased levels of productivity and motivation, as well as a sense of satisfaction and accomplishment.

One of the key differences between distress and eustress is how each makes you feel. While eustress might leave you feeling energized, distress can leave you feeling overwhelmed. For example, if an inexperienced student moves from a rural part of the country to a large city, is expected to perform on demand in school or a new career, is alone, knows nobody, and has to navigate their own finances and budgeting for the first time in their lives, they might be in distress. However, this sort of situation might be seen as eustress to the well-traveled student who is just embarking on another new experience. It is important to distinguish between eustress and distress on an individual basis. We need to know when something can provide healthy motivation and positivity that helps with accomplishments.

Without eustress, people would not be able to function at their best. The clinical psychiatrist Dr. Michael Genovese agrees that stress is popularly seen as a negative thing, but that eustress is beneficial for us. Both exciting and distressing events cause a chemical response in the body (Genovese 2020). This is what makes eustress an important part of our overall well-being.

Theories commonly associated with stress

The James-Lange and Schachter-Singer theories of emotion

The James-Lange and Schachter-Singer theories of emotion similarly state that emotions -- including stress -- are a result of physiological arousal (Critchley 2009; Schachter et al. 1962). According to these theories, your body responds with a physiological reaction when you experience a stimulus. This physiological reaction is then interpreted by your brain as an emotion. For example, if you see a snake slithering across your bedroom floor, your body will respond with an increased heart rate and blood pressure. Your brain will then interpret this as fear and you will feel scared and stressed.

When the body is under stress, the autonomic nervous system -- which controls all of the unconscious processes in the body, such as heart rate and digestion, to maintain homeostasis -- activates a fight-or-flight response. Through this fight-or-flight response, the body prepares for action. The sympathetic nervous system, which is part of the autonomic nervous system, speeds up the heart rate, increases blood pressure, and diverts blood flow from non-essential organs to essential organs. So this theory suggests that you experience emotions -- fear and stress -- after you have some physiological reactions to the new encounter, like startled jumping and an increased heartbeat.

If your boss has just warned you that you need to deliver a project at a ridiculously early deadline, your physiological reactions will come first: increased heartbeat, eye pupil dilation, and perspiration. As a result of your physiological reaction, you will start to experience emotional reactions like fear, frustration, or anger.

The Cannon-Bard emergency theory

The Cannon-Bard emergency theory suggests that individuals react to stressful events in one of three ways: fight, flight, or freeze. However, this is not the result of any physiological reaction. The theory was first put forth by Walter Bradford Cannon in the early 20th century and has since been supported by subsequent research (Bard 1934).

When an individual experiences a stressful event, the sympathetic nervous system is activated, which triggers the release of hormones. These hormones are released to prepare the body by increasing the body's heart rate, rate of respiration, and blood pressure. This response is known as the fight-or-flight response because it enables an individual to either confront the stressor or flee from it.

In some cases, the freeze response may occur. This is characterized by a decrease in heart rate and blood pressure as well as slowed respiration. This response may be more likely to occur when an individual feels helpless or hopeless in the face of a stressor.

Cannon-Bard's theory holds the position that physiological arousal and mental evaluation occur simultaneously. This means that we do not experience emotions because of our physiological reactions. Rather, we mentally appraise the situation as being emotional. For example, if you see a snake on the ground, your body and your brain instantly react. You experience fear because your brain appraises the situation as potentially scary. So your fear is not triggered by your physiological reaction which is happening at the same time.

Cannon-Bard's theory helped lead the way to demonstrate that people with damage to their amygdala (a region of the brain involved in emotional processing) can still experience emotions. This finding suggests that emotions do not require physiological arousal to be experienced.

While this theory has been supported by research, it should be noted that not all individuals will respond to stressors in the same way. Some individuals may exhibit multiple responses or no response at all. Additionally, different types of stressors may elicit different responses from individuals.

The stress theory (Hans Selye)

As previously mentioned, Hans Selye first proposed his stress theory in 1936. Selye observed that when animals were exposed to stressful situations, they experienced a general adaptation syndrome (GAS). GAS is a three-stage process that the body goes through in response to stressors. The three stages are alarm, resistance, and exhaustion. He found that in the alarm stage, the body responds to the stressor by releasing hormones such as adrenaline and cortisol. These hormones increase heart rate, blood pressure, and prepare the body for fight-or-flight. This fight-or-flight response helps the body deal with the immediate threat (Selye 1975).

In the resistance stage, the body adapts to the stressor and begins to resist its effects. This stage is characterized by an increased tolerance to the stressor and the increased hormone levels. In the exhaustion stage, the body's ability to resist the effects of stressors decreases. This stage is characterized by low hormone levels, illness, and sometimes death. However, the reaction to stress may also be positive. Whether the stress is negative or positive -- distress or eustress -- it is a normal and natural stimulus to which our bodies have various responses.

Coping mechanisms

A coping mechanism is an adjustment or adaptation we make in a stressful situation that lessens our feelings of tension and anxiety. Think of it as anything you do to feel better. Of course, it, too, can be either positive or negative. Positive coping mechanisms help you deal with stress in a healthy way. They include things like exercise, relaxation, and social support. Negative coping mechanisms, on the other hand, can leave unhealthy effects on you or the people around you. They may include things like alcohol, drugs, and smoking, to name a few.

Positive coping mechanisms are important because they can help us manage our distress and can make a big difference in how well we cope with it. We all have a coping mechanism for different types of stress. And they vary from person to person and even from year to year for the same person. Each person has a unique relationship with both their stress as well as with their coping mechanisms.

What you find discomforting and tormenting may be normal

for someone else. This explains why some people are more susceptible to adverse reactions in certain situations than others. Their coping mechanisms are different.

Your coping mechanism for a given stress should not be considered negative or bad until it fulfills certain conditions, specifically if it bothers you or others that you care about. When you are exposed repeatedly to the same or a similar stress, your coping mechanism becomes a habit.

CHAPTER 2

HABITS AND LIMITATIONS

"Argue for your limitations, and sure enough they're yours." (Richard Bach)

It turns out that there is a scientific explanation for the phenomenon of habits. It has to do with the way our brains are wired. In this chapter we explore the phases involved in habit development and what to manipulate when you choose to replace an unwanted habit with a healthier choice. I will also discuss some strategies for breaking the cycle and making healthier choices.

This book was not composed to judge you. It is here to help you *Fix Yourself*. Your coping mechanism or reaction to stress is something that you developed as a response to something. It could have been a single exposure or a repeated one. If you have a coping mechanism that you find challenging to stop, change, or that you simply do not want anymore, I want to help you help yourself.

Some people call coping mechanisms habits, some call them addictions, others use the terms interchangeably. Sometimes there is no coping mechanism. Maybe you just feel blocked, plateaued, off, in a rut, or just limited: you are stuck at a certain weight, you always feel that you are inexplicably injured or sick, you claim that you are "not a morning person" or a "night owl" and claim that you cannot change it, you are always late, you are always sad, and so on. People never have a hard time coming up with excuses for not being at their best.

For the purpose of this book and learning how to *Fix Yourself*, let us define some terms to help clarify expectations.

Habit: A settled coping mechanism, regular tendency, or practice that is hard to give up.

Addiction: An obsessive habit for which the victim is unable to find a healthy substitute, to the extent that its cessation is feared to cause severe trauma.

Limitation: A self-imposed restriction that you have perceived in yourself or allowed someone else to influence you into believing. I truly believe that you can do absolutely anything that you work hard at. So there really is nothing that you cannot do. But I am realistic. If you lost your feet to frostbite, you will not grow them back. That is a limitation that I cannot argue against. However, I do believe that you will walk, run, and jump again.

The "five" phases of habit development

Charles Duhigg introduced the habit loop in *The Power of Habit* (2012). He claimed that for every habit there are four phases: a cue, craving, response, and reward. The cue or trigger is what causes the craving. The craving is dealt with by the response, which becomes our habit. The action of the response, or habit, gives us the reward that our brain tells us we need (Duhigg 2012).

1. **Cue**: The cue is the first step in the habit cycle. It is an external stimulus, and it can be anything. It can appear via any of our senses or even just a memory: seeing or smelling food, coming across an old photograph, receiving a note from your boss, being around certain people, hearing a loud bang, something on the television, a song. Reigniting that memory causes feelings and emotions that may be associated with trauma. Similarly, the cue can be an event that causes stress or strain. This could be anything from excessively long hours at work, lack of sleep, and terrible weather conditions, to tormenting pressure, lack of clarity or support, and frustration. If you have ever witnessed how a random object has the power to bring a grown adult to their knees, in tears with psychological stress, you saw how the cue can literally be anything.

2. **Craving**: Cravings are intense desires for a specific activity or thing. When we talk about cravings, we are talking about something regardless of its logicality, healthiness, or security. Cravings can present as physical or mental. The link between the cue and the craving does not have to be apparent. You might know that a certain song makes you crave security and comfort, but you might not recall a childhood memory that would elicit this link.

3. **Response**: Responses refer to the actions that people take that succumb to their cravings. This might involve giving in to the craving and eating the desired food, smoking, sleeping, and so on. When you give in to your cravings, you get temporary satisfaction and relief. In the case of addiction, the response would be using a substance or engaging in addictive behavior. Addictions do not have to relate only to controlled substances.
   If you take caffeine (energy drinks, pills, or even just coffee) to counter the need for sleep, you may feel that there is no substitute. It amazes me how often I hear people saying -- almost bragging -- how they "need" their coffee in the morning. I can assure you that you do not "need" it. But I do understand that you crave caffeine, and it is likely due to insufficient sleep!

4. **Reward**: The reward is the reinforcement that people experience when they give in to cravings. It is what satisfies your brain, be it a certain type of food, nicotine, or caffeine. It does not even have to be a pleasurable reward -- just something that satisfies the brain's needs based on your history. There is also no set duration of time for which that satisfaction will last. In fact, you might even notice in your own self-analysis that you crave the reinforcement of the reward at shorter and shorter intervals as the habit persists.

5. **Regret**: Duhigg's habit loop has (only) the previous four phases. If he had called it the "unwanted habit loop"

> instead, then I would argue that "regret" would surely follow the reward -- making a fifth phase. When our responses and subsequent brain rewards lead to feelings of guilt, shame, or just make you feel like you should not have given in to the craving, they become unwanted habits.

Several studies have connected emotional stress with impulsivity, habits, and addiction (Sinha 2008; Kwako et al. 2017). So when you experience stress -- any kind of stress -- there is a higher chance that you will develop habits that you may not want. Yet you will find that with the repetition of the same or similar stress, it becomes increasingly harder to shake the habit, and it becomes impulsive and ingrained. But, again, any kind of stress can develop these habits. It can even be eustress. And, just as it took repetition to solidify the response as a habit, it will take time and practice to use eustress to create a substitute response and reward -- a new and healthy habit.

Many of us may recall the famous neurologist Ivan Pavlov and his experiments, most notably with dogs. The most well-known story associated with Pavlov -- whether it is true or not -- is how he would ring a bell for a dog and then follow immediately with food. After repeating this, the dog eventually would salivate at the sound of the bell with no food present. For Pavlov's dog, the cue is the bell. The craving is food, which is shown by the dog's salivation -- even though food is totally unrelated to a bell other than by this forced association. The response is to seek food. And, finally, the reward is to get to eat it.

I doubt that Pavlov's dog ever regretted the food. So the fifth phase only applies to unwanted habits. If you truly have no regrets, then you do not have an unwanted habit. And for each individual, the same habit can be different in the sense that it may or may not be unwanted. It can even change for the same individual at various points in their life.

Similar enough

My primary concern is not why you want to change a habit, addiction, or perceived limitation. That is for you to discover and choose on your own. I just want to help you change it once you have identified it. Though unwanted habits, addictions, and perceived limitations are clearly different, for the purpose of this book, let us assume that they are similar enough to be treated the same. You need to clearly define that which you no longer want. An addiction which is an obsessive habit and a perceived limitation or mindset that is inevitably triggered by a cue are essentially the same -- they follow the same habit cycle.

The common denominator of habits, addictions, and perceived limitations is that they are hard to give up. On a habit spectrum, I would put perceived limitations at the bottom, habits in the middle, and addictions at the top. But, due to these similarities and for ease of reading, I will use the term habit to include addictions and perceived limitations throughout the rest of this book. By grouping these terms, I do not mean to imply that any of them are less important or impactful. I am just trying to find common ground that permits a simplified discussion.

A side note on addiction, regardless of whether a behavioral, a substance, or an impulse addiction: stopping or even changing a learned response may seem impossible for addicts if they fear that overcoming their addictions may signal a lack of regret (e.g., if a husband takes up drinking after his wife's death, he may fear that quitting would mean that he does not miss her anymore). Unfortunately, it is often an unwanted habit that the addict is afraid to deal with. If the emotional response is true for the addict, then it is true. It can be illogically logical or logically illogical. Be true to yourself and realize that, if you have an addiction, you may need professional help.

Your brain means well

The science of how habits work is fascinating. They are created by our brains to help us automate certain tasks so that we can free up mental energy for other things. When we first form a habit, it is a new behavior that requires conscious or subconscious effort to accomplish. However, over time and as the habit becomes more ingrained, it starts to become automatic once the cue is initiated.

By then, our brains start to associate the cue with the reward. And so the cycle becomes more and more entrenched. This is why it can be so hard to break an unwanted habit. Our brains have learned that our response leads to satisfaction. But, if you can become aware of this process, consciously choose different responses, and substitute equivalent, healthier rewards, you can, with practice, reprogram your cravings for the better. You can *Fix Yourself.*

We develop responses to various cues and cravings for good reason. Our brains want us to feel safe and balanced -- sometimes to a fault. But this is normal behavior. We are supposed to form habits. Realize that habits are normal. Your brain is functioning as it is supposed to. We may just need to make corrections along the way.

For example, when we contract the influenza virus or another system-wide infection, our bodies increase blood flow to move our white blood cells faster in order to deal with the threat and, at the same time, increase our core body temperature in an attempt to burn out the virus -- making it harder for them to survive. But if our core temperature rises too high, our brain may have a heat stroke that presents as a seizure with temporary or permanent brain damage, or even death. Sometimes we need to help our body's responses and overreactions. In the case of a high fever, we put an icepack on our head, behind our neck, or take a cool shower. The body was not wrong to increase blood flow nor to increase the core body temperature, but in some cases, it can overreact.

Another example might be if someone were to take up drinking (too much) alcohol after losing a spouse. They respond to the memory cues of their spouse and crave to have their spouse back. The response of drinking is seen as a reward by the brain -- maybe because it causes them to forget. The point is that the brain is satisfied, even if just for a moment. For an outsider to demand that they drop the habit implies that they are judging them or feel that they know a better way for them to deal with their loss. Whether the outsider is right or wrong is irrelevant. Only the living spouse knows what soothes their pain. When they are triggered by a thought of their deceased spouse, in this example, their chosen coping mechanism is alcohol. It only becomes an unwanted habit, by my definition, when they ultimately decide that it needs to be changed or when someone important to them is sufficiently bothered by it that the threat of losing that relationship bothers them enough to seek change. Most importantly, they themselves must be willing to dump their unwanted habit.

How to break an unwanted habit

We all have them. Those little (or not so little) things that we know we should not do, but cannot seem to stop. Whether it is biting your nails, smoking cigarettes, doubting yourself, or spending too much time on social media, or a plethora of other possibilities, unwanted habits can be hard to break. But if you are sick of feeling stuck in the same old cycle of unwanted habits, there is hope. You may have tried to quit, change, or stop your unwanted habit in the past without success. Or, maybe, you made a New Year's resolution to change, but by Valentine's Day, you were back to your old habit. With a little understanding of the habit cycle, a bit of effort and willpower, and using the helpful tips in this book, you can *Fix Yourself*.

Typically, two things need to happen before you deem a

habit unwanted. First, somebody may need to bring it to your attention, although this is not always the case. Sometimes you might notice it on your own. But it usually goes unnoticed until you see or hear yourself in a situation that you previously thought was perfectly normal. Second, you have to care that you might be affecting yourself or someone close to you. If you do not agree that the habit is an issue, then nobody else will likely be able to convince you otherwise. "The other person" who brings a habit to your attention might be a newspaper article or a stranger on the street. You do not have to know them personally.

If you are habitually inclined to wake up, get up, put on running shoes, and run five miles each morning, chances are you are not unhappy with that.

On the other hand, let us assume that when you wake up, you light up a cigarette before getting out of bed. Now assume that your partner does not like waking up to the smell of cigarette smoke (and you want to maintain your relationship). In this case, you might consider changing your habit of smoking in bed first thing in the morning. In this case, it does not mean that you have to quit smoking. It might just mean that you choose not to smoke first thing in the morning while still in bed.

It is unlikely that you can break the habit-inducing cue. Triggers are typically environmental or external. The previous example mentioned waking up. Obviously, waking up would be a difficult cue to break if you want to live. What if the cue is your reflection in the mirror? Breaking every mirror and clean window is not possible. But, more importantly, it would not solve anything. The mirror, in this case, is just a cue.

Knowing what your cues are will help you greatly in being prepared with your responses, but attempting to change or avoid the cue might even have the reverse effect. If the site of a doughnut advertisement on a street corner triggers a craving to binge on junk food, taking a different route would be an attempt to avoid the cue. As you consciously detour around the advertisement, you will most likely imagine the advertisement that you are avoiding. So you are picturing the advertisement -- the cue -- in your mind's eye without even seeing it. If you take that detour often enough, the advertisement might not even be there anymore. In this example, you may have actually made your situation worse. And, to make matters worse, there are typically multiple triggers for the same habit. You simply cannot avoid all the cues.

The craving, if you recall, is the nonsensical link between the cue and the response. The link between a bell and food for Pavlov's dog is just strange. But stranger links exist. The reward is necessary because the brain needs to be satisfied when it is triggered. The goal is not to have any regrets. So that leaves us with the response. You need to deliberately force a new response that can produce a healthy reward that the brain will allow you to substitute for the previous, unwanted one. With repetition, you will *Fix Yourself*.

Once you find a substitute response that you believe will work, asking for help from a support team of friends and family is a great addition. When a slip happens -- and they will -- there is no point in hiding it in shame or guilt. Be kind to yourself. Remind yourself that your brain is functioning as expected. Your actions and hardships are normal. Slips are expected and acceptable. If you choose to have a support team, they will learn this too. There is no support in shaming and guilt-inducing blame. Believing in yourself and visualizing success is also a critical part of the entire process. Your guilt might make you want to slack off or give up completely. But your willpower and belief that you will succeed will prevail.

CHAPTER 3

COMFORT

"Stress acts as an accelerator: it will push you either forward or backward, but you choose which direction."
(Chelsea Ericau)

The typical adult today has allowed themselves to get too comfortable. When you read this, you might instantly think of your discomfort with your finances, relationships, the house you live in, or your career. These are sometimes uncomfortable situations, but there is another angle.

Consider the physical shape you are in, how you eat, and how you spend your days. Are you challenging your cardiovascular system? Are you participating in activities that are fun or good for you? Are your exercise routines good for all parts of you or just for your legs, your arms, or something else, or perhaps even non-existent? Are you always just the right temperature with automated smart thermostats, blankets, extra clothes, hot water bottles, fans, and air-conditioners? Are you too comfortable?

Animals (which, after all, we human beings are) evolved by surviving more efficiently than those species that did not adapt as quickly or as well. They were exposed to famine, drought, cold, rain, heat, and other stresses. They did not have refrigerators, freezers, cans, jars, water vessels, heaters, hot water bottles, or fans. Yet they managed to pull through because the animal body can withstand a great deal of discomfort. As you become accustomed to so much modern-day comfort, you do not put your body to full use and you do not perform as well as you can. The saying, "if you do not use it, you lose it" really does apply here. The result is that you underperform without knowing it. You are not realizing your true capabilities.

Deep down, we all know this. That is why we strive to improve. It happens in cycles. We start out with good intentions. But then, life gets in the way. You may be working two jobs, you may be a single parent, you may be taking care of your parents, going through relationship issues, or some other valid reason. If you think about it, there is always a reason, excuse, or something causing us to procrastinate on doing what we know we should do. New Year's resolutions are great proof of this. Every year, many people make a resolution that they typically think long and hard about. They proclaim their goal, follow it for a month, a week, or a day. But then, by February, they are back to the same habit or routine from two months prior. Can you even recall what your last five New Year's resolutions were?

The stresses and discomforts that our animal counterparts experience in nature are a key. Each time we willingly expose ourselves to healthy, controlled stress -- eustress -- that challenges our comfort, we allow our bodies to shift gears into a range that we may have forgotten we had -- or have not yet used in our lives since birth.

Eustress is a positive form of stress that can motivate us and give us a sense of purpose. Imagine the stress you go through when you are about to have a baby. It seems tough, crazy, exciting, and emotional. The exhilaration and excitement typically outweighs the fear, anxiety, and distress. This applies to both mothers and fathers, though the soon-to-be mother is obviously going through a great deal of physical stress at the same time. The same is true when you are packing for a vacation, getting married, or going on a first date. These activities are typically significantly different from distress. But eustress is not always comfortable either. Like most great things in life, you will need some drive or willpower to benefit from it. But this is also part of the solution.

Keep your power

As stated in a previous chapter, addiction is the most serious of unwanted habits. It is the epitome of unwanted habits on the habit spectrum. And this applies to both substance and behavioral addictions. Marc Lewis is a neuroscientist who focuses his work on addictions. In his books and seminars on why addiction is not a disease, he showed that 85 percent of clinics in the U.S. use the disease model for addictions, and their statistics show that most addicts relapse two to ten times when contrasted with methods that do not treat addiction as a disease (Lewis 2015). One of the key issues with the former method is similar to the Alcoholics Anonymous' 12 step program, where alcoholics are asked to give away their control of their disease -- alcoholism -- to be managed by the group, their sponsor, and God. Similarly, the 85 percent of clinics that follow the disease model ask addicts first to hand their power and control of themselves over to the professionals.

The caveat, however, is that there are disease-like aspects for some addictions. Medical intervention is really helpful in some situations, like opiate addiction for withdrawal symptoms. But Lewis explains that forcing addicts to relinquish their power and control and to do what they are told by the professionals causes an increased belief that the addiction is chronic, and the addict diseased and powerless -- thereby potentially causing more harm. This is part of the cause for the high relapse rates. In fact, belief in the disease model on its own was enough to predict relapses more frequently and sooner. While Lewis focuses exclusively on addictions, I propose that his findings about addictions also apply to unwanted habits and perceived limitations.

Labelling yourself as having a disease is stressful and adds pressure. Instead, if the pressure were taken off you, you might be able and open to determine what the habit does for you. In this way, you are given the opportunity to understand the habit and discover possible substitutes and solutions that do not cause distress to the brain and body -- not quitting cold-turkey, nothing negative. You will feel supported and empowered -- not disempowered. You should make new goals that are yours and are something you look forward to. You need to think of the future and create hope. Your past is potentially painful and unchangeable. Although it can and should be dealt with, the fact is that historic facts are set in stone. Present-you might feel stuck or lost and the windows where you might ask for help in the habit loop are small. Support might not be available in the way you need it at the right time.

It does not matter how many times you are a passenger on an airplane flying from Unwanted Town to Betterville. You always need to be flown there. Only after you research the principles of flight, study the mechanics of an airplane, and learn how to become a pilot can you get there without dependencies. And, if you are motivated enough to get to Betterville, you will do it. So the past is set in stone and the present is a practical challenge, but the future holds hope and promise. If you need help, present-you can get help and be a helper for future-you. So be sure to empower your future self.

The same can be demonstrated with modern-day over-the-counter medication for other habits. Many people who run around on a busy day and come home with a splitting headache will head straight to the medicine cabinet for aspirin or the like to solve their problem, instead of considering that they may not have had any water all day. We are a pill-popping society that looks for a quick solution that a professional prescribes or recommends before we look within ourselves. We will pop anti-inflammatory pills like candy before trying to figure out why blood or fluids are rushing to an area -- why our body is crying out. Or, worse yet, with inflammation, we may just ignore it and assume that our body will handle it on its own without further thought. We may unquestioningly accept that we are arthritic or genetically predisposed to some other condition. We willingly give power to professionals so that we do not have to undergo the discomfort of thinking about it or attempting to better ourselves on our own. We decide too quickly that this is the hand we have been dealt and that it cannot be changed. We assume that someone else will take care of it, someone else already studied it, mass produced it, and had it approved to fix the issue that you are dealing with right now.

This is downright laziness. Admittedly, owning your own issues, listening to your body, listening to your mind, and having hopes and dreams can take significant time, energy, and effort. Yes, it can be uncomfortable. Yes, it may seem impossible. Yes, it will be hard work. But it is worth it. If you understand that you CAN do it and that you DO have the willpower, you WILL *Fix Yourself*.

Conditions

Awareness: Before you can take advantage of controlled self-induced eustress, there are some conditions you will have to create. It is important to separate who you are now and what future-you will look like. First, you must be open to perceiving things within yourself. You need to believe that you are capable of personalizing and evaluating your feelings, attitudes, and behaviors in a given situation. Be honest with yourself.

Change: Another condition required is the willingness to change. You will have to work on changing negative thoughts and perceptions into positive ones because you want to change.

Determination: Self-determination or willpower is a crucial component, but if you are excited about the destination, it will be much easier. Yes, you will struggle. Yes, you will be uncomfortable. Just keep your mind's eye on the destination.

Environment: A self-induced activity may be positive and helpful today, i.e. it may induce eustress. But tomorrow, due to outside factors, it can feel negative and unhelpful, i.e. it may induce distress. The effect of the same activity can also be different from person to person. You are not the same as anybody else. And yesterday's you is also different from today's you. Future-you is not the same as today's you. This is the point. We change daily. And change is good. There may be peaks and troughs, but the trend will be toward improvement. Be kind and patient with yourself. Also, make a habit of checking out the environment around, as well as inside you, several times a day.

Smile: One final condition to create is to learn to enjoy your chosen activities. Although, due to their possible discomfort-inflicting capabilities, you might choose to curse instead, I highly recommend that you start, endure, and conclude each self-administered eustress activity with a smile. Even a forced smile has much more possibility of being contagious through your body than a frown, scowl, or general sourpuss face does.

Consider these conditions as a personal contract you make between yourself and future-you. Nobody will check on them for you. Only you are accountable to yourself.

CHAPTER 4

SLEEP

"Sleep is the best meditation." (Dalai Lama)

Sleeping in is quite comfortable. It can be miserable to leave that cozy warm pod that your body has warmed all night, possibly next to a loving partner. This is likely why many people use the snooze feature on their alarms or have alarms at all. Requiring an alarm or hitting the snooze feature too many times leads to being late, eating faster, eating less, or even eating nothing at all, and then starting the day off either rushed, with low energy, or both.

If you feel low on energy at the start of the day, the chance of gaining energy as the day progresses by going to work or running errands is unlikely. This may lead to being late for meetings, appointments, or forgetting about things altogether. In short, habitually sleeping in is not a healthy thing. If you frequently find that you are sleeping deeply right up until being awoken by an alarm (versus lying in bed awake until an alarm goes off), you have little basis to support the argument that you are not getting a sufficient amount of sleep. The fundamental question is: how much sleep do you actually need?

Rest vs sleep

Rest is different from sleep. A healthy sleep session detaches you from your senses without the use of any substance or pill. When you rest, on the other hand, you are not asleep. It is more like mental rest. Getting sufficient sleep also does not mean you have to do it all at once. Temporary (or permanent) daily naps can give your body the breaks it needs or even the lift it needs to break an unwanted habit.

If you are habitually not able to relax in a way that is right for your body so that you can fall asleep within a reasonable amount of time and wake up every day with a smile, before your alarm has rung, then focusing on relaxing will also help. You might argue that you are relaxing while you are sleeping but, while sleeping, you have relaxed your subconscious. Can you also relax while conscious, awake, and aware? If not, why not?

You can just rest your eyes. They do not even have to be closed. Simply looking off into the distance is very effective for resting your eyes, especially in this age of high screen usage. Rest is letting go and relaxing -- not organizing, calculating, planning, charting, eating, listening to a conference call or audiobook, or driving. To rest is to disengage from the world.

It is counter-intuitive not to rest, and it is when you have the most to do that you likely need it the most. If we just trusted ourselves to perform better when well rested, we would most likely do our tasks more effectively and faster than at times when we push through without rest.

Though different, I group rest and sleep together in this book. You benefit from both. Your immune system, metabolic system, skeletal system, muscular system, nervous system, endocrine system, cardiovascular system, lymphatic system, respiratory system, digestive system, urinary system, reproductive system, and your cognitive function all greatly benefit from both sleep and rest.

However, it is not necessary to add up how long you slept and rested to know how much sleep you had yesterday. It simply does not matter. What matters is whether you woke up with a smile on your face before your alarm clock went off every morning for the past few mornings. If you find that you need to have a midday rest to accomplish this, then so be it. Just try to keep each rest under 30 minutes.

A rest can include dozing off. Keep it between 5 and 30 minutes. Use an alarm clock to limit the nap when you do expect to doze off. Any more than 30 minutes is likely to become a deep sleep which can adversely affect your nighttime sleep. Deep sleep is likely better just once a day and at night. Also, consider not changing your bedtime just because you napped, just as you should avoid napping in anticipation of a later bedtime.

It is also okay to have multiple rests in a day. Just be sure to separate them with some energetic mental and physical time of a longer duration than your rest.

How much sleep?

Controversies have trailed this question among scientists and sleep experts for years. I am not claiming to be a sleep expert, but I am pretty sure that I can provide an all-inclusive and accurate answer to how much sleep you need. The answer is also one that becomes increasingly important as we age. Health, stress levels, work schedules, and home life all play a role in how much sleep an average person requires. However, if you have a medical condition, insomnia, or sleep apnea, you may need to see a professional to get help with your sleeping habits.

If you level the playing field, your need for sleep varies with age, gender, what you did over the last few days relative to what you typically do, what your stress levels (both eustress and distress) have been for the past few days, and more. In general, infants need the most sleep. It is interrupted by the fact that they primarily eat quickly digested food and have few body reserves or realized comforts to sustain themselves for more than a few hours at a time. Therefore, they sleep for a few hours, need food and comfort, and then require more sleep, and repeat. As we age, our sleep needs are reduced. Then, as we continue to age, our needs increase again.

The National Sleep Foundation actually recommends numbers of hours based on a study published in 2015 (Hirshkowitz et al. 2015). A subsequent study found that nearly one-third of American adults reported sleeping less than six hours a day (Sheehan et al. 2019). But this does not prove whether six hours is sufficient, too little, or even too much. It only proves that it is less than what the National Sleep Foundation recommends.

Some people feel that they know exactly how much sleep they need each night. That does not mean that they get what they think they need. They just claim to know what it is. Maybe you are one of those people who thinks that they can function just fine on six hours of sleep, or maybe you know someone who appears to function on even less. Do you think you know how much sleep you need each night? Are you envious of those that claim they require less?

In truth, everybody is different and, every year, the appropriate sleep one and the same person requires may change. It might even change based on what you did that day or earlier that week, what you ate, how much water you drank, the temperature, humidity, and many other factors. The all-nighters that you used to be able to handle in the past are just that -- the past. You are not a static being. Just like food and water, your other needs need constant introspection. On a hot day, you need more water, though nobody seems to question or brag about requiring less water in the scorching heat. So why is it done for sleep?

When you do not get enough sleep, your body does not have enough time to rest and recharge. This can lead to a number of problems, including difficulty concentrating, irritability, moodiness, low energy levels, increased appetite, and weight gain. In the long term, insufficient sleep can also contribute to serious health problems such as heart disease, stroke, and diabetes.

While you might have legitimate excuses for working long and hard to the point of exhaustion, such as deadlines to meet, and responsibilities to uphold where you feel that the only option you have is to get by with less sleep, you need to remember that there are consequences. Serious effects on your mental and physical performance are certain to come eventually, if not occurring already.

The question of how much sleep we need should be reformulated as, "Did I get enough sleep during each of the last few nights?" And the answer to that question is another question: "Did I wake up regularly with a smile and before my alarm went off on each of the last few days?" If you can answer "yes" to the second question, then you did get enough sleep. If not, then you didn't. If your answer was "no", then you need to prioritize changing it to a "yes" as a fundamental step on your path to *Fix Yourself*. That is assuming that there are no underlying issues preventing you from getting sufficient sleep.

Sleeping in with disorders and chronic pain

On the other hand, you can also get too much sleep. Some people may regularly go to bed early, not realize that they are not sleeping adequately, and then still sleep in due to lack of (quality) sleep. So, in some cases, sleeping in can be mistaken for oversleeping. But this is not always the case.

Depression can cause fatigue and make it hard to motivate yourself to do anything, including getting out of bed in the morning. Just like anxiety, chronic depression can sap you of your willpower, drown you in self-pity, and encourage you to stay under the sheets even when you know it is counter-productive. It may just appeal to you as a way to avoid the obvious reality. This phenomenon is so common that it is known as depression napping (Bucklin 2017). Protracted depression or dysthymia can lead to more damaging psychiatric disorders or worse. Consider seeing a professional if you think that you fall into this category.

Sleep disorders like insomnia, sleep apnea, and restless leg syndrome, as well as neurological disorders like Parkinson's disease and epilepsy can make it difficult to get up once you do fall asleep. These conditions and others like them are all likely to impede your physical and mental health, whether they trigger inadequate sleep or too much sleep. Some people may need to use specific techniques, such as relaxation exercises or cognitive behavioral therapy for insomnia (CBT-I) to help correct their unwanted sleep habits. Consider seeing a professional if you think that you fall into this category.

Individuals who suffer from conditions like arthritis, fibromyalgia, endometriosis, migraines, injury, and other chronic pain disorders often find that their pain is worse at night. As such, they may experience serious trouble falling or staying asleep throughout the night. Since many people with such conditions rely on sleeping pills or other substances to get through the night, they often either sleep in often in their bodies' attempt to heal, or oversleep because their body demands it.

Conditions like irritable bowel syndrome (IBS) or acid reflux -- also known as gastroesophageal reflux disease (GERD) -- can cause discomfort and disrupt sleep. Respiratory problems like asthma, allergies, and chronic obstructive pulmonary disease (COPD) can also make it difficult to breathe at night which can lead to restless sleep or waking up frequently.

Anxiety is another common ailment that can make it hard to fall asleep and stay asleep throughout the night. This is largely because anxiety heightens tension in your body systems. The Mayo Clinic warns that whether anxiety is based on childhood, adolescence, or adulthood experiences, an anxious person will most likely experience sleep disorders.

All the conditions mentioned above and more can give you a false sense of how much sleep you actually received or need.

Sleeping in with temporary illnesses

When dealing with the flu, the common cold, a broken bone, a strained muscle, or other acute illnesses, ailments, or injuries, you are not feeling well. So your body needs rest in order to heal. Sleeping more can help you recover from an illness more quickly. Similarly, if you have been burning the midnight oil or working long hours, sleeping in can help you catch up on lost sleep. The same can occur when you are woken by a child, fireworks, a loud storm, a dog barking, a dream, a partner's dream, snoring, or some other noise or bright light. It is reasonable to balance the lost hours, but it is even better to focus on getting regular sleep in the first place so that you do not consistently have deficiencies like this.

Sleeping when you are sick is essential for recovery. Sleep helps improve your immune system so that you can fight off your illness more effectively. Thus, if you are fighting an acute illness, listen to your body and allow yourself to oversleep without concern in such circumstances.

Social media and sleep aids

That aside, in today's age, distractions like social media, binge watching a film series, and gaming can become habitual behaviors that rob you of your sleep.

It can turn into a vicious cycle where one or the other of these habits stimulates your brain too much and you become accustomed to it. Then, when you want to sleep, you find it hard. Oftentimes, rather than dealing with the source of the issue, various substances are used as sleep aids. These can take many forms, such as alcohol, cannabidiol (CBD, marijuana, edibles -- either inhaled or eaten), muscle relaxants, sleeping pills, antihistamines, and many other types of pills taken before bedtime. Others may have difficulty winding down at night or may eat large meals too close to bedtime.

The reason for and choice of sleep aid varies from person to person. Sleep aids may initially be used recreationally, as a form of self-medication in an attempt to cope with another issue, or simply taken up to try and get better rest. Over time, they may become a go-to right alongside brushing one's teeth before bed. Whatever the reason, drug and alcohol abuse can have dangerous consequences.

People who abuse drugs and alcohol are at risk of developing a number of health problems including liver damage, heart disease, and cancer. They may also experience cognitive impairments, memory problems, and difficulty sleeping. In addition, drug and alcohol abuse can lead to accidents and injuries, violence, and even death. The idea here is not to label your possible sleep aid choices as "bad". Rather, it is to help you understand the implications of your wanted and unwanted behaviors. A healthy body and mind should not need the assistance of sleep-aid substances.

One of the most famous sleep-aid stories is the sad case that rocked much of the world on June 25, 2009. At the age of 50, American singer Michael Jackson died of acute propofol intoxication, in other words, of an overdose (Weber 2022). Propofol is a surgical anesthetic used in operating rooms. In major surgeries, propofol is used as a general anesthetic to cause a loss of consciousness. It is believed that Michael first experienced this drug during plastic surgery. It was reportedly administered subsequently by his personal doctor as a means of dealing with anxiety and persistent insomnia. It was reported that he had also previously used propofol to help him sleep while he was on tour in Germany, where his anesthesiologist would "take him down" at night and "bring him up" in the morning. I am not insinuating that Michael Jackson died due to a lack of sleep. But he knew that he needed -- and performed better with -- adequate sleep. Yet he also knew that he had sleep issues. So, instead of dealing with the underlying issues preventing him from getting the sleep he needed, he resorted to substances to force his much-needed rest.

Many justify their actions in similar ways, claiming sleep aids help them relax at the end of the day and other, similar excuses. The fact is that instead of taking sleep aids, our time would be put to better use by trying to find out what is causing our unwanted sleep habits in the first place. This is not an easy fix since the underlying issue is often either unknown, or the sleep deprived are unwilling to face the underlying issue directly.

Whether the sleep aid is social media, television, or a substance, and regardless of whether the use of the sleep aids came first or whether the underlying issues came first, if you tried to correct the situation by forcing yourself to avoid your sleep aids (and without some other form of intervention), you might end up staring at the ceiling for hours at your regular bedtime. This might make you think that you do not need sleep, or you might give up too quickly and fall back into your unwanted habit.

All of these habits can disrupt the body's natural sleep rhythm and make it difficult to fall asleep or stay asleep during the night.

If you are struggling with poor sleep, take a look at your daily routine and see if there are any changes you can make to help improve your sleep habits first.

A fundamental step

Sleep deprivation never leads to good or healthy stress. In fact, we hear about it as a form of torture. We sleep to find balance, rest, and allow our bodies to recover. Our bodies are altered during sleep. Our metabolism changes during sleep. Our central nervous system produces different neurotransmitters while we sleep than while we are awake.

It is clear that getting enough quality sleep is essential for good health. It is not just physical well-being. Your mental balance, sexual health, psychological state, and overall well-being can be affected by your sleep quality. You may not know it, but sometimes, all you need to improve is the quantity and quality of your sleep.

Finding out the "magic" number of hours of sleep you need per night is not a thing. It changes daily and is too dependent on what you did in the days prior. There are no bragging rights for sleeping a low number of hours a night every night of your life. However, if you consistently get up with a smile before your alarm goes off, you should brag! In short, if you do not wake up on your own before your alarm clock rings and are frequently tired or unmotivated during the day, then chances are that you do not get enough sleep. Establishing a regular and healthy sleep pattern, ritual, and schedule, and continually adjusting it as your body's needs change day to day is a fundamental step on your path to *Fixing Yourself.* Getting enough sleep should be the primary focus.

Assuming you think you have discovered the sources affecting your sleep, or even if you have not, it is time to mix it up. Change your behavior. Attend to your social media (if you must) in the morning instead of in the hours before bed.

Preparing the bedroom: Remove any electronics from your sleeping area altogether, except for your alarm. If you do work from your bed or bedroom, find a new place for it. Do not work on the computer in bed at any time -- ever. Create your sleep space as a non-stimulating environment. Try to associate bed with sleep, relaxation, and sex. Change the lightbulbs to low wattage ones. Paint the room in soothing colors. Install blackout curtains. Buy nightlights for the bathroom and hallway to the bedroom. Ensure that the room temperature is not too hot, that you are not uncomfortably sweaty, and that your uncovered face does not get too cold in the middle of the night. Consider safe aromatherapy oils, humidifiers, or diffusers if they help you relax. The diligence it takes to permanently disable the snooze feature on your alarm and to actually get up when you wake up is notably difficult. But do it anyway.

Getting ready for bed: Create a relaxing bedtime routine including winding down for at least 30 minutes before bedtime in a way that does not include a phone, tablet, monitor, television, or other types of screen time. Keep a cup of water by your bedside. If you require bright lights or sounds for things like brushing your teeth or washing your face before bed, then they should not be considered part of your 30 or more minutes of winding down time. Be sure you own a comfortable bed, pillows, sheets, and blankets. A hot shower or bath can be handy to relax you before bed if you do not need to complete it with a loud hairdryer or the like. Consider a white noise machine for the duration of your sleep time. Just do not use your phone, tablet, or computer -- they are no longer in your bedroom anyway, right?

During the night: During sleep hours, keep the bedroom cool, dark, and quiet. Ensure that you do not need to turn on a light in the hallway, bathroom, or kitchen to use the facilities or to get a drink in the middle of the night.

Waking up: When you wake up, whether before the alarm or not, immediately get out of bed BEFORE shutting it off. Leave the bedroom quickly. Consider brushing your teeth first if you do not already do so. Gargle water or mouthwash loudly so that it makes you laugh (it helps a lot!). Wash your face with cold water right afterwards. If you do not usually shower in the morning, start doing so. Make your bed right away so that it does not look so inviting to climb back in. Do *not* get back in.

If you have bigger issues: Seek help from a qualified sleep specialist if self-help measures are not enough to ensure that you are getting sufficient sleep.

Our bodies seek regularity. So, if you are a night owl who is trying to get to sleep earlier in order to learn how to be more of a morning person, going to sleep early may seem hard for a few weeks. Anyone who has experienced jetlag knows this. Be patient and consistent. New, better, healthier habits take time to set.

As you read through the rest of this book to find solutions and help in order to overcome your inexplicable disorders, humps, plateaus, and unwanted habits, first plan to check in on and change your rest and sleep habits if you are not waking up with a smile before your alarm each morning. Sleep on it.

CHAPTER 5

BALANCE

"Everything in moderation." (Cleobulus of Lindos)

Achieving balance is essential for leading a healthy and fulfilled life. It means creating a healthy equilibrium between work and play, family and friends, alone time and social time. Achieving an overall life balance can help reduce anxiety and stress, improve your mood and energy levels, and promote physical and mental wellness. Equally important is that it stimulates productivity. Creating a life balance may look different for everyone. It depends on your unique circumstances, values, and goals.

As peachy as it sounds, achieving a life balance is torturous for many people. For example, you may be a full-time student, work two jobs, have a spouse and children, a social life, time-sensitive goals and dreams, or a combination of these and others. If unbalanced, the physical and mental distress may also lead you to develop unhealthy habits such as sleep, diet, and exercise issues. You may understand the concept of balance and know where you are lacking, but, if you feel like you are running around trying to keep all the juggling balls in the air, then you likely have not prioritized balance. If so, you are not alone. Studies by the

World Health Organization (WHO) and several other research institutions indicate that an unhealthy balance between work, play, and self-care is why many people cannot maintain their well-being, cannot prevent burnout, and do not feel successful in their personal and professional lives (Burton 2010; Lupu et al. 2021).

It is possible to channel all efforts towards one thing at a time. However, it is focusing on only one thing for too long that earns this topic its own chapter. You can eat just chicken for breakfast, lunch, and dinner and be just fine for a while. But, after some time, you will need some vegetables and other dietary staples. Each thing you choose to do or even think about should have a timeline that is balanced with the other things of importance in your life.

Ensure that each necessary facet features in your life and is given appropriate focus. The problem is that everybody is different, has different goals, different needs, different spouses with different needs, different children and pets, different jobs, and different body types and ages. It can be difficult to achieve balance in just these cases, let alone the hundreds of others you might think of. This is precisely why balance is personal. You must find the balance that works for you. By setting aside time for the different areas of your life and taking care not to overdo anything, you can create a balance that will help you feel happier and more fulfilled.

Procrastinating and multitasking

If you procrastinate to the point where you are chronically late and are unproductive but you are not bothered by it nor by the people you put out, and you do not think it is bad, then it is not a high-priority unwanted habit.

But if you are not accomplishing goals and are not being productive, you could be a procrastinator. The things you do in an attempt to not do what you know you should be doing should be considered an unwanted habit. Many chronic procrastinators may actually be either diagnosed as obsessive compulsive or may be borderline obsessive compulsive to some extent. They strive for perfection and do not want to accept anything less. While that is a difficult goal to argue against, their goal of perfection is flawed if they produce nothing. It is worse yet if they cause themselves distress because of it.

Other procrastinators are convinced that they are fabulous multitaskers. I am sorry, but multitasking is simply not a thing. Even if you are convinced that you are a fantastic multitasker, consider just for a moment that you might be wrong, and challenge yourself to do just one thing with 100 percent focus. If you are unable to focus all of your energy and attention on just one thing when you consciously choose to, then your claim to be able to multitask is that much weaker.

Imagine how effective our ancestors, the cavepeople, would have been when hunting if they multitasked by gathering roots while simultaneously taking aim with a bow and arrow. It would not have made for a successful meal. Though the hunt was just as important as the gathering, they knew that 100 percent focus was necessary. Or, maybe, just the ones that figured that out lived to evolve. Sadly, we may need to relearn this to prevent ourselves from facing a similar fate. Just because we can go to the grocery store now does not mean that those focusing skills are no longer useful to us in other areas of our lives. Maybe the excuses or labels you have allowed to be placed upon yourself have you convinced that you cannot change these things.

Richard Bach said, "Argue your limitations, and sure enough they're yours." If you have accepted your limitations, then you will not change them. When it comes to doing something -- anything -- give it your undivided attention. But give it for a balanced amount of time. Then, tend to your other priorities in increments that are proportionate to your priorities -- all of your priorities.

How?

In case it is not clear to you how you can roughly plan your time or focus proportionately, pick a topic and a duration. Let us use eating as an example. Say you chose to eat according to the 1950's diet of a balanced Four Food Groups. I am not saying this is correct, good for you, or recommended. It is just an example. In this example, you chose to balance each meal. You would ensure that 25 percent of your breakfast was grain, 25 percent was milk-based, 25 percent was fruit and vegetables, and 25 percent was meat. If, however, you chose to do the same diet but preferred to balance over a day and chose three meals per day, you would then make sure that each of the same percentage of each food group was eaten at some point over those three meals. So, if you wanted to have milk-based foods only in the morning, then 75 percent of your breakfast would have to be milk-based, but then you are done with milk for the day. Alternatively, you might only choose to balance the four groups over a week, in which case a cheese fondue for dinner might cover a big chunk of that milk-based portion for the week.

In the 6th century BCE, Cleobulus of Lindos wrote, "Pan metron ariston" (παν μέτρον άριστον) which translates to "Everything in moderation". Here it can be applied to say that moderation is better than lack of control. If a slip will demoralize you, then it is best to accept moderation. The logic of how to consciously deal with cues, cravings, responses, and rewards may be clear. But your body may not be so easily convinced.

Using what we consume as an example, so many things that we deal with have certain allowances for things that are not inherently good for us. The Center of Disease Control (CDC), Environmental Protection Agency (EPA), Food and Drug Administration (FDA), World Health Organization (WHO), and others all have recommendations or regulations. As an example, chlorine is a deadly poison. Poison control centers have dedicated web pages to help quickly diagnose chlorine poisoning although there is no antidote. Yet we drink it every day. Over 98 percent of U.S. water supply systems that disinfect drinking water use up to 4.0 mg/liter (4 ppm) of chlorine as a disinfectant.

That is not to say that this is a bad thing. Quite the contrary, the real danger, when it comes to chlorine, is eliminating its use due to the chance of bacterial contamination. The point is that even chlorine is consumable in moderation. On the other hand, regular and safe drinking water can be considered a poison. In fact, over 300,000 people around the world die every year of water poisoning. It is the third leading cause of unintentional death worldwide -- also known as drowning. Too much of a good thing can also be bad for you. "Everything in moderation."

Similarly, apply this to your work life, family time, and personal time. You learned from the last chapter that you need to budget about 60 hours of sleep per week at this point in your life. Maybe you would like to spend one third of your time at work, one third for personal time, and one third as quality family time. If you chose that for a week, for example, there are 24 hours in a day and 7 days in a week -- therefore 168 hours in a week. Let us say 60 of those hours are for sleep which leaves 108 hours. Though your goal is one third of time at work, you might have a 40-hour-per-week job which makes that impossible without giving up on something. If I did a good job of convincing you in the last chapter, you should not give up on sleep. So you are left to split quality family time and personal time between the 48 cumulative hours left in the week. That is about 31 hours of the weekend and almost 7.5 hours a day to split between family and personal time. You did not achieve your goal of spending one third of your hours on family and personal time in this case, but the week does not include holidays and vacation days. So, maybe, you can redo the calculation over a month or a year to ensure that your goal is met.

The point is that you choose your own goals. It does not matter what they are. Only you can be true to yourself and judge what you want and need. I am just identifying that if you think that sitting in the living room with your family while they are watching television and you are working on your computer counts as multitasking on both work and family time, then you are doing a disservice to both your employer as well as to your family. One hundred percent engagement with your family does not include television or your work.

I was looking for a replacement vehicle years ago and came across a used car salesman who was connected with a mechanic's shop. While waiting for the salesman, I spoke with the mechanic who was working on an old vehicle that I had never seen before. It was a 1960's Amphicar Model 770. I was so fascinated with it because it is an amphibious car (both boat and car). I asked the mechanic if it was a good vehicle. His response was very memorable. He said, "It is about as good as anything that you use for multiple purposes. It is equally a crappy boat and a crappy car."

Use whatever analogy you want to substitute here but, if you check your work email while on a date, your multitasking makes you both a "crappy" employee as well as a "crappy" date.

Cognitive dissonance

Cognitive dissonance is the term used when we do something that we know is bad for us. I am pretty sure that all smokers have read the Surgeon General's warnings on every cigarette pack, but they still smoke. Oftentimes the stress of knowing that you should not be doing something is worse than the unwanted habit itself. Constantly pressuring yourself to change your behavior and repeatedly fighting against yourself, and then beating yourself up for failing or caving in magnifies the ill effects. Conversely, slipping back into old habits is all too easy to do because we are not hard enough on ourselves or we lack willpower. We get comfortable in our routines and before we know it, we are right back where we started.

Just as with the pendulum of a clock, there is an extreme one way. And there is an extreme the other way. We have to find our own balance and constantly adjust to find the middle ground that we are aiming for.

Logic vs application

Unwanted habits are ultimately caused by emotional distress or boredom. The emotional distress can be a product of a past physical occurrence or a traumatic experience. Whether due to boredom or distress, it is important to be gentle and patient with yourself. If you are vulnerable to feeling the guilt from failure, then recognize and remind yourself of this often. Forgive yourself in advance. Expect, allow, and plan for slip-ups as you support yourself to change.

In martial arts, coordination has been defined as the synchronization of the mind and body. Even precisely coordinated dual hand motions synchronized with stepping can be learned with repetition. But when triggered by an attacker, all logic goes out the window, and whatever has been dominantly rehearsed takes over. That might still be an unwanted habit.

For a tamer example, if you have never tried to pat your head with one hand and rub your belly with the other, you might not succeed the first time. It might be possible to think it through thoroughly several times before trying a second time with success. Try it now.

If you succeeded just now, was it your first time? Try it again now with the opposite hands. It is likely that you have heard and tried this popular example before, so let us try something a little less common.

Basic waltz box step: Start standing with your feet together. Step left with your left foot on the count of one. On the count of two, step forward with your right foot. On three, bring your left foot up next to your right. On the following count of one, step right with your right foot. On two, step back with your left foot. On three, bring your right foot back next to your left. Repeat: 1,2,3,1,2,3.

Now repeat that basic waltz box step four or five times. Continuing the basic waltz box step with your feet, pat your head with one hand and rub your belly with the other at the same time. Now have someone set off firecrackers that whiz past you in directions and do not stop the box step or hand motions. You can skip the firecracker part. I think you understand my point. This is what some triggers may feel like to people who are trying to apply their logically sound and well-rehearsed substitutions for an unwanted habit. It can just be too much and too overwhelming. How do you compete with something like that?

My first car: If you were like me and could not afford a new or decent first vehicle, sometimes a less desirable vehicle had to be purchased. My first car cost $400. I did not have an emergency fund to fix something if it broke, and a rattle developed. The only alternative was to turn the stereo volume up louder than the rattle. I fought fire (crackers) with fire. While this is not a safe or recommended solution for driving vehicles, it does set the stage well for dealing with unwanted habits that are causing us distress.

Rhetorical questions

Here are some more appropriate examples than my first vehicle.

The cold wolf: In the great white Northern winters, how does the wolf -- a non-hibernating species like the human -- stay warm when they cannot turn up the heat, put on an extra layer, or fly south for the winter?

The deep-diving seal: How does the seal hold its breath underwater longer than it can out of water?

The sleepy grizzly bear: How does a grizzly bear hibernate for six months every year without eating?

The hungry lion: Who will win a fight between a lion unfed for a month versus a lion fed well daily?

Anthypophorae

The responses to all these questions have a similar answer, which is also the answer to where we find the fire to fight back. In short, the mammalian body is amazing. The only difference between the cold wolf, the deep diving seal, the sleepy grizzly bear, the hungry lion, and you is that you are the only one who has not regularly used your mammalian powers on a regular basis for your entire life.

As a response to the external stress of cold, the wolf naturally produces neurotransmitters with its central nervous system and various glands throughout its body such as the pituitary and adrenal glands. These trigger the body to redirect blood flow to their vital systems, yet maintain sufficient blood flow to the extremities so as to prevent frostbite.

When cold water touches the face of the seal, a message is sent via the vagus nerve which slows the heart rate of the seal down so that it uses less oxygen and, therefore, can hold its breath longer since it uses its oxygen more efficiently.

By hibernating, the grizzly bear alters its heart beat and core temperature so that it can easily survive over six months without food. This is triggered by brain activity and blood pressure. The brain activity even starts prior to actual hibernation where the bear still eats normal amounts but is already in a lower metabolic state. The bear will not even defecate or urinate while in hibernation. After six months without eating, they awake without a loss of bone density or muscle mass. In fact, females can even give birth while hibernating.

The lion's body has grown accustomed to eating large meals and then fasting for long periods before the next meal. It is still a top predator when unfed, even for a month. In fact, being too well fed might be a detriment. Just recall your last turkey dinner and how lethargic you likely felt after over-indulging.

Learning to unlock similar mammalian powers can help you do amazing things, one of which is to help you with your unwanted habits. This is the balance we can use. This is the fire that we will fight back with. But we will do it without having to face what the wolves, seals, bears, and lions have to endure.

Our ancestors: Like us, it is believed that early hominids also did not have thick fur or much hair. They certainly did not have central heating, electric blankets, or a computer to maintain a constant temperature in a car or house. When cold, they warmed themselves. But they did not do it actively or consciously. They just did it because there was no other choice. When they were hungry, they could not go into the pantry with a can opener to open up something preserved from weeks before. They just waited for their next feeding opportunity.

There are many more mammalian feats like the camel or kangaroo rat that can go six months or years without water, respectively. The advantage they have is that they have further evolved and adapted their bodies for specific environments. We are not looking for such a big adaptation. We want to expose ourselves to just enough eustress to trigger our bodies to concoct a mammalian power cocktail from within.

Introducing stresses (eustresses) like these on a smaller and controlled scale (in moderation) yet at regular intervals will unleash similar neurotransmitters in your body to light a fire in you from within. This is the fire that will help shake things up to reset your body into realizing that it is time to change and adapt using tools that your body has shelved for far too long.

In the next chapters, we will introduce you to methods to stress your bodies in slow, controlled ways involving movement, food, oxygen, water, touch, temperature, and music. For best results, you should consider several or all of these eustress methods. So read on and prepare yourself for amazing experiments to unlock your mammalian powers!

CHAPTER 6

BEFORE EXERCISE

"Strength does not come from physical capacity. It comes from an indomitable will." (Mahatma Gandhi)

When it comes to applying eustress to your body, challenging your perceived limitations, and substituting unwanted habits, there are few better activities than exercise. You have surely heard it before, and you know that exercise requires focus, grit, and determination to be effective. Exercise is necessary for good health. But, here, I am not talking about a gym membership. I am talking about basic body movement to keep your bones, muscles (including your heart), and lungs in shape.

However, there is a realization that you may have to make. You may not be as young and athletic as you remember. Or maybe you never were. If it has been a while since you did your favorite exercise, you have a greater chance of injury. It is not necessarily because you are out of shape, but every year that you age, your recovery takes longer. When you do not regularly stress (eustress) your bones, they lose density and become brittle. When you do not regularly challenge your muscles, their tendons do not get sufficient blood flow and pull or tear more easily than expected. Unexpected injuries like these at the beginning of a push to start a regular exercise regime are very demotivating and leave poor memories and associations with exercise when reconsidered in the future.

How many times have you heard or known an elderly person who falls and breaks a bone -- typically a hip? It is unlikely that the same fall would have broken their hip 40 years prior. Sure, their balance and reflexes have diminished. But more importantly, their bone density has reduced. So how do you keep up your bone density? Have you ever thrown a ball as hard as you could without warming up, and your arm hurt the next day? Yes, a warm up may have helped, but why? The concept is the same as with bones. With diminished blood flow, the tendons are not sufficiently hydrated and lubricated. It would be like pulling on a rubber band that has been in the freezer -- snap! As mentioned in Chapter 3, "if you do not use it, you lose it". Speaking in rough averages, our bones reduce their growth in length when we are 16 to 18 years old. Your peak bone mass will be reached roughly between the ages of 25 and 30 years old. By age 40, we start to lose bone mass. Men typically accumulate more bone mass than women during their growth phase (NIH 2022; NA 2011). However, genetic limitations regarding bone length does not speak for bone density. You have surely seen women who, even structurally, look more solid than some men.

These things are closely tied to genetics. The amount of calcium you ingested during key growth years, the amount of sun (vitamin D) you were exposed to at key ages, and many other factors are what get you close to your genetic potential. True, the length of your bones might not be easy to increase beyond your full genetic potential at your peak age. Similarly, the age you are when your bone mass peaks and when you start to lose bone mass might not be possible to alter either. It is for reasons such as these that people typically just assume that their fate is sealed.

However, none of these published limitations are truly functional. They are averages for the general population of the human species based on the sample size and demographic that a given research article included. Even then, each publication has the possibility for variance. So even though you may not be able to change your potential maximum height, reach, or other bone length and you are unlikely to be able to alter the age at which you reach your maximum bone density, how much or quickly your bones start losing mass can absolutely be manipulated with eustress.

There is no way to accurately gauge your bone density's rate of decline or how fast your tendons weaken. It is different from person to person. You have to listen to your body. But what does that mean? I, too, do not know how to listen to my body per se. Maybe there are people who can, but I am not one of them. However, I did not want to settle for that, so I did the next best thing I could think of. I decided regularly to test my body's limits instead.

If a senior with a broken hip had regularly and purposefully practiced falling in a controlled manner regularly, their bones would have been slowly eustressed and thereby built up in response to the eustress. Your bones do not stop responding if they are used (Friedman 2009).

Similarly, if you threw a ball gently 100 times per day and

then increased the intensity and speed of the throws slowly and steadily every day, you would be less likely to get injured by a single throw off the couch. Your muscles and tendons will be used to having high blood flow to them. The eustress of daily, controlled throwing would have been eustress that conditioned you for throwing.

Yes, you can

Of course, there are other factors involved like sleep, diet, distress levels, and more. But exercise certainly plays a major role. The point of this chapter is to emphasize that you might not be able to run a full 26.25 miles just because you have run a marathon in the past. You might pull a calf muscle at mile three if you have been inactive for too long. And that is okay. Acknowledge that you may need to start off slowly and avoid injury because an injury will surely set you back even farther.

When you first start exercising, if you are not accustomed to exercise, your body tries to conserve energy and will resist your efforts. This is why it is so important to start slowly. You may also have heard people say that they are not runners. Maybe you are one of them. It is one of the most ridiculous limitations people can argue for themselves. Sure, it hurts them. That is because they have not done it regularly. I am not telling you to buy a pair of running shoes. If you do not like running and do not want to do it, that is fine. But own that you can run and could run well, fast, and far if you chose to put the effort in. You just might not choose to. If you acknowledge that and believe it, we can move on. If you are set on a limiting and negative mentality, you will likely struggle longer. People have an amazing ability to make up excuses to argue themselves out of doing things.

Perceived limitations are those self-imposed boundaries that you believe are holding you back from achieving your dreams. They keep you trapped in your comfort zone and prevent you from taking risks. They can be based on your past experiences, your beliefs about yourself, or what others have told you. Overcoming these unwanted habits requires you first to identify them and then to take action to change your thoughts and beliefs.

One of the most common habits is the belief that you are not good enough. If you believe that you are not good enough, you will not even try to achieve your goals. You need to challenge this belief and prove to yourself that you are capable of anything you set your mind to.

Perceived limitations (habits) are only as real as you make them. You need to challenge each one and find ways to make more time for yourself. Identify your unwanted habits, face them head-on, and you will be one step closer to achieving your goals.

I believe in you. You can do anything that you work hard at.

Bodhidharma

You cannot do what you did in your childhood or even last year and expect to perform the same if you have not been putting the work in along the way. You will likely be sore the next morning or worse -- injured. Once your body gets used to the exercise, it will start to cooperate and you will see the results of your hard work. Be kind to your body, especially if you have ignored it for too long. There is no shame in starting slowly. In fact, starting slowly and gradually increasing your intensity is often the best way to avoid injury and ensure long-term success.

According to Asian folklore, Bodhidharma was a South Indian Buddhist Monk who lived around the fifth century. He had trained in the ancient martial art of Kalaripayattu in his youth, and he was efficient at it. Buddhism inspired him to travel to China where he lived in a cave in the hills near a village with fertile fields and a monastery. Because of their crops, the village often attracted bandits who would come and raid the village and the monastery. After witnessing this a few times, Bodhidharma could not understand why the villagers would not defend themselves, so he approached them and asked. They claimed that they simply did not have the skills to fight. So Bodhidharma took it upon himself to teach them what he knew.

However, upon beginning their training, he noticed that they were not even in good enough shape to do basic martial training drills without risking injury to themselves. They had fallen out of shape and were simply too fragile. He rethought his teaching strategy and developed what became three text books of bone and tendon hardening exercises. These included theories and simple exercises like jumping up and down, punching the air, deep tissue massage, and light bone stress (eustress). These were essential before more serious martial arts could be practiced.

Once the body was gently prepared for exercise, it could then be challenged and trained to do amazing things over time. That village was called Shaolin, and that monastery is now referred to as the Shaolin Temple, from which all Chinese and Japanese martial arts were derived.

The point here is that, if you have not kept up regular exercise, you will need to be kind to your body and start out slow. If not, you can suffer injuries that will take much longer to heal than what you likely remember from your youth.

As our bodies age, our unstressed bones lose density and become brittle. Our muscles, tendons, and ligaments lose their elasticity. Even running regularly throughout childhood and into your 40s will likely result in injury if you do not supplement your running with other exercises. The supporting muscles will tweak, pull, or tear more easily if they are not isolated with rehabilitation-like physiotherapy. Someone who rolls and falls repeatedly and purposefully until they are in their 70s will be less likely to break a hip when they fall than the 70-year-old who walked carefully and avoided any impact or jarring for the last 20 years.

Pre-exercise exercises

Here are some exercises and goals to consider building up to if you feel that you have fallen out of shape. Even if you have not, these are great daily exercises to do. You should remember that you do not need to reach these goals. The act of introducing this new, light, controlled eustress is the goal in itself. Take your age, general health, and history of physical activity into account before pushing too hard.

1. Bounce lightly on grass or a mat without leaving the ground. Eventually, build up to 100 jumps in a row as high as you can on a hard floor without hurting your ankles, knees, or hips.

2. Slowly punch the air with fully extended arms. Eventually build up to the point that you are giving a full effort without blowing out your elbows' ligaments for 100 punches in a row.

3. Using a chair or pole, guide yourself from standing to a slow and full (butt-to-heel) squat. Eventually build up to 50 slow squats without support. Similarly, build up to sitting in the squatting position with heels down until it is comfortable for several minutes. For both of these, keep your hands, elbows, and arms off your legs or hips.

4. Lie on your back with straightened arms above your head. Then, lift your straight legs, straight arms, and shoulders simultaneously to touch your hands to your feet. Build up to 20 repetitions.

5. Lie on your stomach with straightened arms above your head. Then, lift your straight legs, straight arms, shoulders, and head simultaneously for five seconds, 20 times.

6. Build up to holding a push-up in the upper plank position for one minute.

7. With one knee on grass or a mat, do a front roll over one shoulder 10 times. Repeat over the other shoulder. Take care not to roll over your head because it risks neck injury.

These are activities that a child would likely do with ease, yet we have chosen to sit in chairs most of the day instead. Moving your joints in ways that you have not since childhood, using muscles that you forgot you had, eustressing bones lightly and in healthy ways, and allowing tendons and ligaments to be tried again will increase blood flow to them, strengthen them, and prepare you for other exercises and activities. Along with the increased blood flow come neurotransmitters that your body will throw in as it "wakes up" from lack of sufficient movement as an almost-forgotten reaction to eustresses like these.

It is no secret that starting an exercise routine can be daunting, so do not forget to be gentle with yourself. Be patient and kind with yourself. Also remember to be positive about the entire process. Starting any exercise routine is an opportunity to reconnect with your body and mind. It is a chance to move your body in ways that feel good, to tune into your breath, and discover what your body is capable of at this point in your life -- listen to your body.

Trying to change too many things at once may jeopardize your efforts, so remember to be systematic about your progress.

Often feeling cold: If you find that you are cold throughout the day, especially when you are indoors, consider that it is not the weather's fault. You are likely too sedentary. If you did any of the pre-exercise exercises listed above every time you felt cold rather than fetching an extra sweater, turning up the heat, drinking a hot drink, or eating a hot meal, you would be using eustress appropriately by changing your response to your craving to not be cold. This is an example of how unwanted habits are broken.

A bit more on Bodhidharma

Bodhidharma taught "a special transmission outside the scriptures; not founded upon words and letters". In other words, Bodhidharma believed that the true path to enlightenment could not be found in mere intellectual or academic study. Instead, it is found in self-experience.

The zen tradition emphasizes direct experience and intuition rather than reliance on scriptural authority. Bodhidharma emphasized the importance of mindfulness and meditation as a means of achieving enlightenment. He believed that when we realize our true nature, we will be enlightened. Reading about this alone will not be sufficient. You have to act.

Practice also allows us to develop skills and knowledge. The more we practice, the better we become at whatever it is we are trying to do. We can use this skill and knowledge to accomplish anything we set our minds to. So, if you want to accomplish something, remember to use both reason and practice.

Decide on what you want to achieve. It does not have to be the "right" goal. It just has to be something that is a change from what you no longer want. Convince your mind to put aside the excuses and be willing to do it. Then, put in the hard work required to make it happen. This means making time for your new habit every day and consistently sticking to it. Doing less but doing it daily is far better than doing something weekly or two to three times a week. Daily repetition builds habits faster, but introduce change in reasonable and attainable steps. The more you practice, the easier it will become, and the easier it becomes, the more likely you are to stick with it in the long term.

Here is an example in case you want to start jogging but find that you typically would rather sleep in. Again, start small and grow:

1. For a week, just aim to wake up 30 minutes before you need to be up, but get up and out of bed. Put on your running clothes that you laid out the night before, and put on your socks and running shoes. That is it. Repeat just that daily for at least two weeks. What will happen is that you will slowly train your body to get up. It does not really matter what you do for the next 30 minutes so long as you do not go back to bed or lie down somewhere else.

2. When you find that getting up 30 minutes early is less of a problem, that it is not that bad and you have built confidence in yourself, congratulate yourself. Now, for the next two weeks minimum, after getting your running gear on, step outside. Stay outside for at least 10 minutes -- rain or shine. Do anything you want while outside dressed in your running gear for those 10 minutes. Enjoy the fresh air.

3. Congratulate yourself if you have accomplished that. Now start walking around the block in your running gear each morning for 10 minutes. Speed or distance does not matter. Just walk. Do that for at least two weeks every morning for at least 10 minutes before carrying on with your day.

4. Once again, be proud of yourself. Graduate to the next level of changing your walk into a jog. Do not go farther than you were walking. You will be done faster which, in itself, may feel like a treat. Again, continue this for two weeks every morning. Avoid rest days. You are not overexerting yourself, so there should be no need for days off.

5. Now build your jogging time up to 10 minutes for two weeks, then 15 minutes for two weeks. How long or far you choose to jog is totally up to you and your own goals. Build up to a marathon if you choose. Or just remain at 10 minutes. You are running! You are a runner! You did it!

Again, apply the simplicity and slowness of the progressions in a way that gradually prepares your body -- eustress versus distress. At no point should you be distressed in this controlled approach. There is no race. There is only action. Believe in yourself. I believe in you.

CHAPTER 7
MOVEMENT

"Life is like riding a bicycle. To keep your balance, you must keep moving." (Albert Einstein)

Over the last chapter, we established that exercise is a great way to improve your general health, but we need to prepare ourselves so that we do not overexert or injure ourselves. But to many, exercise might have a negative connotation. Some associate exercise with hard work. Although it is and that should be welcomed for the purpose of *Fixing Yourself*, what I really mean by exercise is movement. So, if it helps you to do more, then call it movement. Our ancient ancestors were in constant motion, whereas today's average person is comparatively sedentary.

A regular increase in your daily movement will improve your overall mood, increase your energy levels, and reduce long-term distress and tension, even though your movements might tax and challenge your body. When you are distressed, your body releases hormones that can lead to short-term physical symptoms such as headaches, chest pain, and a rapid heartbeat. This does not even take the long-term negative health effects into consideration. Movement will help counteract these effects by releasing neurotransmitters which have mood-boosting and pain-relieving effects.

In addition to its physical properties, exercise can help reduce the levels of the stress hormone cortisol in your body. Cortisol is the primary stress hormone that alters immune system responses and suppresses the digestive system, the reproductive system, and growth processes (King et al 2002; Galbo 1983). Studies have shown that regular physical movement of an adequate duration can also help improve memory and cognitive function (Angevaren et al. 2008; da Silva et al. 2015).

So, if the thought of getting a gym membership causes you distress -- either the thought of having to go, the cost involved, or the guilt in thinking that you might not keep using it -- then do not fear. You can find other ways to move. Similarly, if you believe that the thought of running will cause you distress -- although I think it is a wonderful form of movement -- take a deep breath and relax. There are other activities to choose from to achieve similar results. The main goal is to get your body moving to the point that you are forced to breathe deeply for, ideally, 30-45 minutes. This time span is just a rough guide. I do not believe there is a mathematically accurate way to work out the number of minutes you should exercise, mostly because everybody is different. But, also, it depends on the type of movement you chose, the heart rate it incurs, your age, what your exercise history is, whether you have had injuries or surgeries, what you have eaten in the last few days, how much sleep you have had in the last few days, and so on. So, if you are of a senior age and trying to get back into movement, go easy on yourself and do not think you need to hit 30 minutes on the first day. Similarly, if you are in your twenties and have no history of injuries, you can likely aim to build up to 45 minutes in a short span of time. But there is no pressure regarding duration. You set your own goals. As long as you can honestly say that you are challenging yourself and are out of your comfort zone, then you are on the right track.

Three main focuses for movement

Bones: Your body is designed to move, receive force, and adapt. A 2014 study by Dr. Stuart J. Warden showed the cross section of professional baseball pitchers' throwing arm bones (humeri) were consistently more dense than their non-throwing arms. The unique torsional force created by the repeated mechanical load in throwing gradually causes a slow buildup of the bone density to compensate for the eustress (Warden et al. 2014). When a bone is unused, it becomes brittle. On the other extreme, an over stressed (distressed) bone will break, fracture, or have damaged joints or ligaments (ligaments hold bones and joints together). But eustressed bones are allowed to grow more dense in preparation for future stress.

Muscles: Muscles connect to your bones via tendons. They need regular movement to stay strong and healthy. Without regular use and nutrition, the muscles and tendons will experience disuse atrophy -- they become weaker and smaller. If you have ever had a friend or family member who was bed ridden for a month or longer, you will have noticed how quickly their muscles visibly reduce in size. Movement prevents that. Physiotherapists use passive movement on paralyzed and comatose patients to assist in muscle movement and blood flow to both speed up their recovery as well as to maintain circulation -- even if the muscles will not be usable again.

Healthy body movements help to maintain or improve muscle strength, mass, and function. But, oftentimes, people go through a New Year's resolution type of situation. They make a new promise to themselves to start the new year off with some exercise regime that is harder than they are ready for in their current circumstances. It is typically a goal chosen without enough thought, based on what they did in their youth, what they think they simply should be able to do, or the result of comparing themselves with someone else who can do the activity to that level. To prevent overdoing it, ensure that you build up to be able to repeat your chosen form of movement daily as discussed in the previous chapter. If, for example, you bust out 100 minutes of some rigorous activity but cannot walk the next day, you have overdone it. Muscle protein synthesis is a slow and steady process. You have to be patient and kind to your body if you expect it to perform reliably for you. Lactic acid is produced mainly by muscles and is a natural and expected byproduct. But too much exertion will generate too much lactic acid production, which is why you feel muscle pain and discomfort. Your body has fallen behind at processing your lactic acid. This leads to a high exercise failure rate because the new habit has not been given a fair chance to set. Doing one day "on," followed by skipping a day, is a quick way to fail at most attempted habits.

Eustress in the form of movement that is planned reasonably

with a long-term objective in mind is a key ingredient to preparing your body for what it was designed to do -- move. We are not supposed to be sedentary organisms. The movement you build to will not only strengthen your muscles and tendons but will also trigger the production of neurotransmitters that support your immune system and your ability to deal with inflammation. When you work muscles too hard, they experience distress and strain, tear, become damaged, or otherwise injured. When you train them with thought and care, they react to the eustress by building in preparation for their next exposure to stress. Ultimately and if done carefully, what would have been distress without preparation can be built up to with eustress.

Heart: With increased motion, the cells of the muscles being used require more oxygen as well as the removal of waste products like lactic acid. This is done via blood cells. To move the blood cells, your heart must pump faster than when you are just sitting on the couch. But the heart muscle is also a muscle. Although it never stops beating, it does need rest in the form of not working too hard for too long. Just as muscles and bones can rip, tear, and break under distress, the overworked heart can lead to many health issues including heart attack. But, just as muscles and bones can be prepared over time with eustress, the same can be done for the heart. The term cardiovascular is derived from the Latin word for pertaining to the heart -- *cardi* -- and small vessel -- *vasculum*. The increase in heart rate works hand-in-hand with the constriction of the blood vessels to allow for faster delivery of blood. Recall that when you use a garden hose without a nozzle, the water just pours out. But, if you restrict the opening with your thumb, you can shoot the water quite far. Your central nervous system has the same ability, but along the entire length of your blood vessels instead of just the end. In a healthy situation of eustress, this is ideal behavior. However, when the heart is ignored, abused, not adequately maintained, insufficiently nourished, or lacks rest, excessive and prolonged high blood pressure can result. This forces the heart to work harder to move blood when it actually needs rest.

Additionally, eustress increases levels of high-density lipoprotein (HDL) -- the good cholesterol -- and helps to prevent plaque buildup in the arteries (Assadi 2017). With plaque buildup, your blood vessels experience the same symptom as blood vessel restriction. It makes the heart work harder for prolonged periods with minimal to no time for rest.

Bones and muscles, including the heart, need rest -- sleep: a fundamental step to self-improvement.

Eustress #1: Daily movement that works bones, muscles, and heart

The Mayo Clinic recommends that you calculate your maximum heart rate by subtracting your age from 220 (Mayo 2021). For example, if you are 45 years old, subtract 45 from 220 to get a maximum heart rate of 175. The maximum is just that -- the maximum. Superseding that is not recommended. A moderate heart rate is 50-75 percent of that maximum. A vigorous heart rate is 75-85 percent of your maximum. The Mayo Clinic recommends 150-300 minutes of exercise per week, with 75 minutes per week at a vigorous level. But, as with all numeric recommendations like this, only you can know what is best for yourself, your situation, and your medical history.

However, when exercised time is stated in time per week, I believe it is misleading. If you only went running on Sundays from 9:00 am until 11:30 am or 2:00 pm and nothing more, I do not believe it would be as beneficial for you as running for 20-40 minutes per day. The slow and repeated application of eustress has much more underlying power than the distress of once a week. It is also harder to establish a habit when exercising only once a week rather than daily. Rest days are not necessary if you never overdo your chosen movement activities.

A key point of this chapter is for you to consider whether you may have the unwanted habit of insufficient movement in your life. You might avoid exercise out of laziness or procrastination. You might make the excuse of not having anyone regular to do it with or to encourage you. Or maybe you simply do not know which activity to do. My goal is to help you make sure that you find activities that will give you the biggest and quickest results for your time. At the same time, you do not want to risk injury, so please be sure to read the previous chapter on pre-exercise exercises.

Choices: The choices are really endless. What really matters is that you choose activities that include all three categories of your bones, muscles, and heart. For bones and muscles, you will want to incorporate movements that include as many of your bones and muscles as possible. If your favorite activity is swimming, that may work your muscles and heart quite well, but it does not offer significant bone eustress. Similarly, weight lifting is wonderful for muscles and bones, but it is not what we want for the heart. You might argue that your heart rate and breathing increases when you do a set of 15, but I can also get your heart rate up just by startling you. We are chasing eustress. I encourage multiple activities for this reason as well as for the fact that most activities focus only on one or a few movements. Although you need your upper body in running and bicycling, you are not doing your upper body justice by just swinging your arms or holding yourself in position. Please do not misunderstand though. It is most certainly better than no movement. But we are aiming for gold here. If time in your day is of concern, consider activities that cover all three categories of bones, muscles, and heart.

In your quest for the ideal movement activities, your childhood memories might want to introduce ones you may have enjoyed doing in the past. Enjoyment is key in making your choices something that you stick with. Activities like bowling, golf, billiards, walking, and curling are fine things to do, and I encourage them. But they are not the type of activity that should be considered here for this purpose. You want a healthy challenge to your bones, muscles, and heart. Whatever type of movements you choose, make it something that you enjoy and that you are able to stick with on a regular basis. Set yourself up for success. Your movement choices should be those that reduce your distress, not add to it. There is often a thin line between distress and eustress. Set realistic goals for yourself and strive to improve gradually. Make sure that your workout is challenging enough to give you a sense of accomplishment, but not so difficult that it feels insurmountable. You want to feel like you are pushing yourself and making progress, but not like you are constantly struggling just to keep up. That would not be enjoyable.

Remember that eustress is all about balance. Do not go overboard with your workouts. Make sure to leave some time in the day for relaxation and recovery as well. If you push yourself too hard, you may end up feeling burned out and distressed instead. If you are too sore or tired the following day to do the next movement exercise, then you have gone too far. Add variety to your workouts to keep them interesting and balanced. Above all else, listen to your body.

A quick note on walking: Walking is a wonderful activity, but not strenuous enough to challenge the bones, muscles, and heart in the way we are aiming for here in this chapter on exercise. Walking can improve circulation and blood flow throughout the body, which can help reduce distress levels even when the stressors are still present. It can also help to clear your mind and allow you to focus on positive thoughts rather than dwelling on negative ones. However, it makes a great warm up or stepping-stone activity as you work up to more intensity. There is, however, a way to turn walking into a eustress activity. Make a special note to read Chapter 13 to find out about it.

Here are some common examples of eustress movement activities and exercises, including my thoughts regarding which areas they typically focus on.

Running: (lower body bones, leg muscles, heart)

Running is one of the most natural exercises for humans. Our ancestors needed this skill, both to escape predators and to be the predator. If you have not written it off as unpleasant and are willing to build up to it, start slowly with just the routine discussed in the example in Chapter 4. Consider running on the spot or jumping on a rebounder (miniature indoor trampoline). If you still cringe at the thought of running, realize that it is a necessity for the human species. Without the ability to run, we would not have evolved. We would not have been able to hunt or fight effectively. Thoroughly consider whatever excuse you might be making that has you set in the limited and negative mindset that you are not a runner, dislike running, or cannot run. If you have not done it for a long time, or if you have never run, then I would agree that it might be very uncomfortable to start now. But that is precisely what we are looking for here -- eustress; getting out of your comfort zone. If you have two functional legs and will not run, then you may as well have a full set of teeth and ingest nothing but soup. So please reconsider running -- not racing, not competing; just a slightly faster walk with brief airtime between each step.

Jump rope: (lower body bones, leg and shoulder muscles, heart)

Many of us have not jumped rope since grade school. It is such a simple activity that can be done even with an electric extension cord, but I would highly recommend a proper speed rope for a more enjoyable experience. You will notice that the jumping part is what relates this to running. The eustress of impact is what is desired to stimulate the bones, from your feet all the way up through your vertebral column.

Dance: (leg muscles, heart and more depending on the type of dance)

Too many people are socially afraid of dancing in public places. If you find yourself in that category, then this can be a solo activity in the privacy of your living room. Turn on the television or YouTube and select whatever type of music and dance suits your taste. Imitate, learn, let your body do whatever moves it feels like doing. Attempt to keep a rhythm. But more importantly, have fun.

Weight training: (muscle, bones if heavy weights)

Weight training does not have to be in a gym, but if going to a gym is the push that you need, then by all means go. You can use a brick, a skillet, or whatever objects are around you. Or you can purchase barbells, kettlebells, or any number of training tools out there if you wish to get fancier. Just realize that weight lifting is rarely a great heart exercise.

Swimming: (muscles, heart)

Swimming is a low-impact activity that can provide many health benefits. It is a great muscle workout for the whole body and can help to improve cardiovascular fitness. However, it is missing the bone eustress that we are looking for. Do swim if you enjoy it, but be sure to supplement it with a bone intense activity.

Yoga: (muscles)

Yoga, if done correctly, is fantastic for muscles, but there is little bone or heart eustress involved. Additional benefits to yoga include relaxation and breathing practices, but do supplement it with other activities.

Martial arts: (depending on the style: bone, muscles, heart)

An art like boxing will cover all three categories. You do not ever have to get in a fight or even a ring though. Boxing training exercises on their own make for a fantastic eustress workload.

Other arts like Tai Chi, Aikido, and Qigong are amazing practices, but they typically lack the level of eustress we are looking for so that the bones, muscles, and heart are all targeted.

Finding exercises that cover all three areas and that are enjoyable to you may be tough, which is why I recommend several. And the best part is that you do not have to stick with any activity that becomes unfun over time. The main point is to select movements that eustress your bones, muscles, and heart.

Rolling (somersaulting): (bone)

Rolling is so simple and effective. It was mentioned in Chapter 6 as an exercise to condition yourself to exercise, but it is really conditioning yourself for falling. I feel it is important enough to repeat here.

Start slowly. Starting with one knee on grass or a mat, do a front roll over one shoulder 10 times. Repeat over the other shoulder. Take care not to roll over your head because it risks neck injury. Eventually, build up to rolling over your shoulders from a squatting position. Then, build to a standing position. There is no need to push farther, but if you have built up this exercise regularly for a long period of time, you could even attempt to jump into a roll.

The benefits are not just for your bones. It also ensures that your organs are supple and mobile. If you keep up your rolls, it will be significantly more difficult to fall and break a hip as a senior. That usually happens when people are afraid to fall, forget how to fall, or have become too stiff to not hurt themselves if they lose their balance.

Let's get moving!

CHAPTER 8

EATING

"To eat is a necessity, but to eat intelligently is an art."
(François de la Rochefoucauld)

What this chapter is not

You are probably expecting an "eating" chapter to talk about what you should and should not eat or maybe the next Atkins, Keto, Whole30, or other weight loss or health improving diets that have hit the mainstream. All of them have great intentions and justify how they meet the recommendations of professionals to stay or become healthy. However, that is simply not what this chapter is about. It is true that you should do your best to eat healthily, try to figure out which foods work best for you, and in what proportions. But that is what the previous chapter on balance was about. It is okay to eat candy and chips. It is okay to drink alcohol. It is okay to have a cigarette. But only if you can do it in moderation and proportionately to healthy things. If you need that cigarette daily, then it is no longer okay. If you have to drink every day, it is no longer okay. If you only crave candy and chips when you are hungry, it is no longer okay.

And everybody is different. Therefore, following someone else's diet might help you open your eyes, but it is unlikely to work or have the same effect on you at this current moment in your life.

It is of key importance not to be a slave to your assumed or self-inflicted habits. Maybe, in addition to insufficient sleep as discussed in Chapter 4, your habit trigger is the anticipation of what you have convinced yourself you need in the morning. Do you head directly for coffee upon waking up because you have convinced yourself that you "need" it? Consider letting your body become accustomed to waking itself up after a full night's sleep without the assistance of caffeine. I do not believe that coffee is bad for you, but consider that "needing" it might not be the healthiest option. Why not have that same cup of coffee a few hours later or with lunch instead?

It is amazing what we think or can convince ourselves that we need to consume. Take a bag of chips for example. Do you really crave that full bag of chips? I would bet that just the taste of one or two would give you the salty or savory taste that your taste buds might want. But the entire bag -- even just a small one -- is simply not necessary. It is a potato. Would you eat a baked potato to quench the same craving? I doubt it. Consider this type of rationale for other things that you think you need. If you are true to yourself, you will be amazed. Test yourself, experiment, and learn about yourself.

There are so many diets out there and I am certain that there is a benefit to each of them. Recently, I felt like I was not digesting foods the way I thought I was supposed to. I mentioned to a friend that I might be slowly losing my ability to digest certain foods. They called me out on my self-proclaimed limitation and challenged me to eat unpasteurized, organic sauerkraut for one day -- even just for one meal. I did it and repopulated my digestive tract with up to 28 distinct probiotic bacterial strains that sauerkraut can contain (Lu et al. 2003). Of course, I was not aware of this until I researched it after the fact. Maybe it was due to another issue. After all, I did not apply this experiment using a valid scientific method. I just ate. I did not trust that it would do anything for me just once. I did it every few days for a couple of weeks. Research has shown that sauerkraut can help reduce gas, constipation, symptoms linked to Crohn's disease, ulcerative colitis, irritable bowel syndrome, and diarrhea (Trakman et al. 2021; Didari et al. 2015). On a side note, overeating on sauerkraut will overwhelm your digestive system and you will have temporary diarrhea, so be warned. It happens to me within 4 hours, but I am back to normal in less than 8 hours. Even knowing this, I still do it. I still overeat on it. But I enjoy the benefits thereafter, knowing that my digestive tract is being populated healthily. Knowing this allows me to continue eating what I want. To me, it is worth a little bit of a mock diarrhea.

My point is that any and every diet is just a diet. I encourage you to change and experiment how you eat and to do it often. Try every diet fad that crosses your plate. Learn what your body likes and does not seem to like about each one. Do not just try it once. Sometimes your body will be a little shocked and will need a few tries to get used to something drastically new. Again, you change at every stage of your life. What did not work last year might work this year. Many children have childhood allergies that they outgrow. Some do not like foods like tomatoes until they are into their 20's. Our ancient ancestors were forced to eat seasonally. Those that lived in regions that experienced ice and snow in winter had relatively low sources of greens in their diet for those months and more meat. It is a positive thing to try new things often and see how your taste buds and bowels change. Just do your best to stay away from processed foods, white flour, white rice, jams, sweetened juices, canned vegetables, and processed meats. Those have been proven to cause entire societies to suffer with more cavities, severely crooked teeth, obstructed airways, and overall poorer health (Price 1932).

What this chapter is

Studies from Penn State University, Dakota State University, and several others have established that there is a connection between what a person eats, how much a person eats, and their mood (Wegner et al. 2002; Swayne 2013). People who consume a diet high in processed foods are more likely to experience depression and anxiety than those who eat a diet rich in whole foods (Ljungberg et al. 2020; Lachance 2015; Hecht et al. 2022). Similarly, eating an overcooked or dissatisfying meal may leave you in a sour mood, which can affect your productivity. Eating sugary foods may also give you a quick burst of energy, but a crash will follow it. That pretty much sums up what I would like you to eat. Now, let us get on with the main meat of this chapter.

Although the type of food you eat may cause distress, I am

more focused on how much you eat. The point here is not to lose or gain weight. The objective of this chapter is to show you a controlled eustress that will give your body a kick in the right direction.

We are living in a time of abundance when it comes to food. If you are reading this book, you are likely not a starving citizen of a third world country. Most of us are not limited by what we eat for the year based on what we sowed in the fields. If our tomatoes do not fruit, we go to the grocery store -- if we even grow our own food. Having such easy access to such a diverse range of foods, even when they are naturally out of season or not even native to your region, is a feat of the modern world that we take for granted. Just think about the distance your bananas or coffee must have traveled to get to you. Because of this ease of access we tend to overindulge.

The right amount

What, then, is the right amount to eat? And how often should you eat so that you have just the right amount of fuel to keep your brain sharp and your mind creative?

The cold hard fact is that we may be thinking about this all wrong. European settlers were thought to be the ones who introduced three meals a day as the healthy way to live. Then there were articles written promoting theories that frequent meals throughout the day were more efficient for maintaining metabolism to battle weight issues. This was humorously reinforced with the "proper" Hobbit daily diet of breakfast, second breakfast, elevensies, luncheon, afternoon tea, dinner and supper.

But what if these forced meals were the start of poor eating habits? Do we need to eat as many as three times with brunches, desserts, and everything in between? What would happen if we did a less extreme version of the lion (from Chapter 5) who does not eat for a week or a month?

Unfortunate people who live in true poverty in third-world countries (and even first-world countries), enslaved people, those caught in political or wartime battles, and many others go for entire days without food due to lack of money or lack of food itself. Sadly, they experience more than just true hunger. In addition, they also live in fear for their lives, of abuse, torture, and other horrific things. Yet a good number of them survive. Tragically, many do die of starvation (among other reasons), so there is a limit to how much food deprivation our bodies can withstand. Most of us will hopefully never know this type of hunger. But it leaves the question, where is the limit?

If we just focus on eating -- so assuming that we are not fearing for our lives and are not experiencing political or wartime battles -- how can we turn the distress of forced hunger into eustress to unlock the secret mammalian superpowers that come along with it?

By way of illustration, consider some other examples.

Gandhi: Mahatma Gandhi went on 18 public hunger fasts in his lifetime. The longest was 21 days. This means three weeks with nothing more than sips of water.

Monks: Customs vary by region, but many Buddhist monks eat only between sunrise and noon. Some only eat when they are offered food and may not ask for it.

Ramadan: During Ramadan -- the annual lunar month and one of the five Pillars of Islam – a devout Muslim will abstain from food and water (as well as tobacco and sexual relations, among others) from sunrise until sunset for 28 days.

Our ancient ancestors: Our ancestors -- the Denisovans; *Homo habilis, erectus, neanderthalensis, floresiensis, naledi, troglodytes*; cavepeople -- did not have refrigerators, freezers, cans, or jars to preserve their food for later. Whatever they gathered or hunted had to be eaten right away or soon after as only a little could be kept for later. Because of this, they could go without food for days until they found their next meal. Their hunger is thought to have triggered neurotransmitters that enhanced their immune system, senses, and other mammalian powers. Their body systems were active and constantly motivated, fueled by these unlocked benefits as a result of the reasonable eustress of hunger.

Fasting for health: I am not going to ask you to do any of these. Gandhi's fasts were long. Monks' eating styles are kept up daily and for life. Ramadan is for all daylight hours for a month. You do not have to repeat what our ancestors endured. We can do something a little more reasonable. However, know that others have done and do these things regularly while continuing with their lives, business, and school during these periods. A healthy human body is extremely resilient and can go for several days without food without any lasting effects. Hunger pangs do not and will not kill you if you allow them to happen willingly and in a controlled manner. In other words, cutting out food and experiencing hunger does not hold you back. In fact, like for the lion, there are health benefits that come with hunger. Similarly, fasting periods can benefit you as a detox period because it allows the release of excess waste stored in the body's fat reserves and encourages organs to make better use of its temporarily limited food supplies.

No one has a final answer as to how much food a person should consume. There are many guidelines. The Food and Drug Administration (FDA) estimates that an adult requires roughly 2,000 calories per day, with the caveat that the number varies depending on age, sex, height, weight, and physical activity level. What is clear is that we can survive on far less than we consume, meaning we are typically overeating, thereby generating an unnecessary set of problems in our systems that may impede our efficiency.

So the answer to the question of how much food to eat is, quite simply, to eat less. When you do eat, do not eat until you feel full. Do not snack if you are not actually hungry. I am willing to guess that you can reduce your consumption by half. But to simply "eat less" might sound hard. If it does not, it *should* sound hard because it is. Counterintuitively, this is actually secondary. Cutting down on the amount you consume is breaking an unwanted or series of unwanted habits. In order to help you and your body learn how better to control what you consume, the correct eustress to apply is regularly to feel hungry.

Symptoms

Caveat: Exceptions to the following statements might apply for those with pre-existing medical conditions like diabetes, anorexia nervosa and other eating disorders, epilepsy, multiple sclerosis or similar health conditions. In addition, I would not encourage anyone who has suffered from an eating disorder to fast without medical supervision. Unfortunately, those suffering from eating disorders may be all too practiced at not feeling hunger pangs.

Fatigue: When fatigued, most peoples' default belief is that they have low blood sugar and just need food. The same excuse is often made when feeling cranky or angry. "Hangry" is the modern pun for hungry. More precisely, it refers to irritability or bad temper as a result of feeling hungry. How is it that Gandhi, monks, Muslims during Ramadan, and our ancestors have been able to function normally with over eight hours between periods of food consumption, yet modern-day people experience "hanger"? The dots may not be easy to connect, but oftentimes the real issue is a lack of sufficient sleep, the habit or routine of eating or snacking, or some other conditioned and self-inflicted habit. You can also get tired when you eat too much. Think of your last Thanksgiving, Christmas, birthday, all-you-can-eat, or some other meal where you knowingly overate. The fact that you are overeating -- versus undereating -- may seem difficult to accept because you have conditioned yourself to consume as much as you do. Yet, when you think about it like this, it will likely not seem odd to you.

If you eat often enough, you might not even have to overeat before you feel tired. The feeling of being full is triggered once your body identifies that it has had more than it needs. So the point where your body consciously perceives that it is "full" may be a step higher than your body's actual needs. It is often said that our eyes are bigger than our stomachs. This is typically only stated when you dish up more on your plate than you can finish. When hungry, you will think you are hungrier than you actually are and put too much on your plate. In addition, you have most likely become accustomed to eat fast, chew less, and swallow more than necessary in one sitting. Imagine the result if you always filled yourself to the brim. My guess is that most people do not require much imagination to picture this. Overeating is a daily habit for most people. In fact, overeating may be your key unwanted habit or go-to for dealing with other distress in your life.

Mood swings: Similar to fatigue, your mood can be an excellent means of determining distress. Many will assume that their low mood is related to low blood sugar because it is easier to blame that than to dig into deeper underlying issues and distresses. However, unless you have a pre-existing medical condition, mood is unlikely to be food-related, even though eating may seem to stabilize you.

Nutritional deficiencies: Your body needs nutrients such as proteins, fats, carbohydrates, vitamins, zinc, and many others to become healthy, maintain health, or gain health. Again, I am not going to tell you what to eat. Refer to Chapter 5 on balance. The amount and what you consume can cause large amounts of distress -- more so when done repetitively.

Compromised health: Obesity is just one possibility of overeating. Overeating has been hypothesized to be a contributing factor to many other chronic diseases like heart and fatty liver diseases, type 2 diabetes, stroke, and various types of cancer. If overeating is a potential cause of major diseases like these, I think that it is very likely a source of many other easy-to-ignore, missed, or misdiagnosed issues. It is easy to assume that overeating is linked to more directly associated conditions like indigestion, heartburn, constipation, irritable bowel syndrome (IBS), gastritis, and other gastrointestinal problems. However, I would go a step further and dig deeper into any form of inflammation, whether local or systemic. Since everybody reacts and responds differently to the amount and types of foods they require at different stages of their lives under different circumstances and environments, you can assume that you will present issues differently as well.

Despite the staggering implications of overeating, it is easy for anyone to fall into its trap. Mahatma Gandhi, Muslims during Ramadan, monks, and our ancestors have all shown that the human body requires far less in order to thrive than most people consume.

Eustress #2: Weekly controlled food deprivation

The eustress introduced here is a reasonable form of fasting. Just as I recommend testing and changing your diet often to learn about how you might have changed, you are also changing the regularity of your diet. Rather than allowing your body to expect food, you will prepare it to possibly go without. You are training your body to expect the unexpected by not being predictable. Although you will not be adopting the fasting patterns used by Gandhi or Muslims during Ramadan, you will be fasting intermittently.

When you fast, your body is forced to burn stored glucose as energy. This process, known as gluconeogenesis, can help regulate insulin levels and prevent spikes in blood sugar. In addition to regulating blood sugar, fasting has also been shown to lower cholesterol and triglyceride levels (Yuan et al. 2022; Phillips 2019). It improves heart health by reducing inflammation and improving blood pressure. Many studies have shown that fasting can improve memory and cognitive function and protect the brain against age-related degenerative diseases such as Alzheimer's and Parkinson's (Talemal 2021). Studies on animals have also shown that fasting can extend lifespan by protecting cells and tissues from damage (Hwangbo et al. 2020). The National Library of Medicine says, "All in all, metabolic, cellular, and circadian mechanisms of fasting periods have direct and indirect influences on the brain, which subsequently could improve cognitive functioning and the prevention or progression of brain-related disorders" (Gudden et al. 2021). All this points to the fact that fasting potentially promotes longevity.

Rather than hitting the extreme end of the spectrum like Gandhi or fasting from sunrise to sunset for 28 days like Muslims during Ramadan, consider building up to a regular fasting ritual that is much more easily attainable. For example, aim for once a week on Mondays. That means building up to eating nothing between Sunday's dinner and Tuesday's breakfast. Drink just water for all of the Monday in between. You will have to learn how to deal with your hunger pangs until they simply disappear. Until then, you will need to use your willpower, but you will quickly learn that you do not *need* food for that full Monday -- you only *want* food. Something about chewing and snacking is really all that you miss. After four to eight full Mondays of fasting, you will find it becomes more of a slight inconvenience than a struggle. The hunger pangs will no longer be a problem for you.

Do not change any of your regular routines though. Your fasting day should still include the activities you would normally do. Get a full night's sleep on the Sunday night prior. Wake up and do your regular movement routine. If it is a day on which you typically go jogging, do not stop that activity, especially if it is eustress as discussed in this book. Just skip breakfast, coffee, tea, and juice. Go to work. Do not change your work schedule (except for lunch meetings). Instead of eating on your lunch break, go for a walk. At dinner time, join your family at the table and engage in conversation. Then, consider turning in to bed early. The next morning (Tuesday), enjoy a healthy breakfast, but do not overeat.

Everything else stays the same. Just remove all food and drink consumption and substitute it with water from after dinner the night before until breakfast the day after. Remember, fasting for one full day a week cannot physically hurt you. You are learning to break through the shackles of hunger pains. Consider less fortunate people who cannot afford or find food for days if you are doubting your ability to fast for just 35 hours (from after dinner on Sunday until breakfast on Tuesday).

As long as you are healthy, you are not going to die from not eating for a full day -- about 35 hours. If you feel shaky or faint, sit down. Also, be sure to read Chapter 9 on breathing. It will take a few tries to adapt, trust, and learn. Your body needs a few iterations to snap out of its dormant state of a hibernation of sorts. Pay attention to your body and how it feels. Listen to your body.

Your fast does not have to happen on Mondays. That is just the least impactful day that I chose to make work for me. It was not my first choice, but it ended up being the best fit after trial and error. Find what works for you. If you feel that you have to build up to it by skipping just one meal at a time, then that is fine, but make sure you are challenging yourself. Without pre-existing medical conditions, there is no harm in doing the full 35 hours immediately on the first try. However, more than once a week is not necessary. Just make sure you are safe and make sure that you repeat it weekly as a regular practice.

This chapter is not intended to promote a certain diet. That would mean telling you what to consume. The recommendation here is to consider not eating anything for one full day per week on a regular basis. The purpose is to teach and train your body for eustress that it does not often feel -- hunger.

The hungry lion is given the advantage of neurotransmitters that are only released when their central nervous system feels hungry. They have more to lose if they miss the next meal than the lion which is stuffed full. So their body gives them an advantage. Behind the scenes, your central nervous system will be accommodating the eustress from your fast. It will kick in neurotransmitters when it notices the lack of food. You just have to give your body a chance to relearn this mammalian power. It might take a few iterations before you no longer feel lightheaded at certain times of the day, but, at a minimum, after the first few times, you will have the confidence and knowledge in yourself that you can make it through the day. Once you have attained that, unwanted habits like snacking will present themselves. You will be left with the conundrum of knowing that you do not need food during that day and that the desire to snack is the result of boredom, stress, distraction, or any number of other reasons. The calories you did not consume on fasting day may also give your body the shake needed to get a better night's sleep. It might even happen immediately.

This eustress on your system might be the wakeup-call you need to help your body realize that a sweet treat, cigarette, or cup of coffee is not as desirable, fulfilling, or necessary as an apple. The human body is an amazing thing. Give your body the chance to prove it to you. Food for thought.

Reminder on balance

When you do eat, your eating style, preferences, or choices should not be relevant. Just be sure to be balanced and proportionate. There is nothing wrong with eating cookies, so long as they are proportionally less than your vegetable intake. The same applies to alcohol, caffeine, tobacco, soda/pop, potato chips, and so on.

But my guess is that most of your life has been spent overeating. I challenge you to balance it out now by discovering that you can learn to fast one day per week. In doing so, you will prove to yourself that you have been overeating all this time as an unwanted habit. You do not have to change what you eat if you choose not to. The eustress challenge is to limit how much you eat and to balance it all well. "Everything in moderation."

CHAPTER 9

OXYGEN

"Control your breath, control your life." (Unknown)

John Smith: On Monday, January 19, 2015, 14-year-old John Smith from Missouri, U.S., was submerged in Lake Sainte Louise for over 15 minutes before emergency services could pull him out of the freezing cold water. The emergency crew performed CPR for 43 minutes without him having a pulse. He walked out of the hospital on his own on Wednesday, February 4 -- just 16 days later. The movie *Breakthrough* (2018)was based on his story.

Chris Lemons: In 2019, Chris Lemons was working as a deep sea saturation diver and was disconnected from his team's ship when a cable supplying communications, air, and heat suddenly snapped. He was stuck 300 feet below sea level in the North Sea before his crew could get to him. He went over 30 minutes without breathable air but was revived with CPR.

David Blaine: In the two instances above, the loss of oxygen was accidental, but David Blaine has made a name for himself by challenging his physical limitations. He studied and trained since he was a teenager to build up his ability to hold his breath. As an adult on the Oprah Winfrey show, he held his breath for over 17 minutes while submerged in water. He never lost consciousness. He did not need resuscitation. This feat was regarded as one of the most profound effects of human willpower.

Ancient Greeks: Ancient Greek armies are thought to have demonstrated their coordination and demoralized their Persian adversaries by chanting as they marched. To chant loudly while marching requires good posture, deep inhales, slow, controlled exhales (while singing or chanting), and coordination with physical activity (marching).

Other armies: This type of chanting has since been enhanced into the call-and-response military cadence used while marching in most armies in the world today. At least in the U.S. military, it was noted that sustaining this type of chanting while marching regulated the body's balance and energy (Salley 2015). This might help to explain how Napoleon Bonaparte moved 200,000 men 500 miles to Vienna in 40 days.

How much oxygen

Just like food, we need oxygen. With too little food, you starve and die. With too much food over a sufficient period of time, your health will suffer. But with the regular and controlled eustress of fasting, you will unlock your mammalian superpowers.

Similarly, with no oxygen for too long, you suffocate and die. With too much oxygen over a sufficient period of time, your health will suffer. But with the eustress of regular and controlled oxygen deprivation, you will also unlock mammalian superpowers. But what are the limits?

Too little oxygen: Clearly, those who have tragically suffocated and drowned had insufficient oxygen for too long a time. You have to physically be deprived of air containing sufficient amounts of oxygen for this to happen. It is not that easy to do. For this to happen, either your lungs have to fail to pull fresh and oxygenated air into them, meaning that your pumping blood cannot extract oxygen from your lungs, or you have to be placed in a situation where oxygenated air is unavailable to you.

If you were to hold your breath simply by closing your mouth and not breathing through your nose for long enough, you would eventually faint (please do not try this). But if you nevertheless did do this, after fainting, your resilient human body would automatically make you breathe in your unconscious state. You simply cannot hold your breath long enough to kill yourself without some other form of oxygen deprivation. Generations of children have threatened to punish their parents by holding their breath for not getting their way and, although some may have fainted, none have died from that empty threat to date. That is not to say that they may not hit their head or cause other trauma as they faint, but, then, the cause of injury or death would not be oxygen deprivation.

The point is that, if you are healthy, in a well ventilated area with access to ample amounts of oxygenated air, and nothing is manually blocking your air intake, you are going to have a hard time dying due to oxygen deprivation.

Too much oxygen: It has been claimed that hyperventilation-type breathing is a way to super oxygenate your blood so that you feel a bit of a caffeine-like boost and possibly perform physical feats you did not think possible. Others argue that this is, instead, a method of decreasing the carbon dioxide in your blood and your body's reaction to it so that the urge to breathe is temporarily more easily fought off. When speaking of these types of breathing, it always involves breathing the same atmospheric air which contains about 21 percent oxygen at sea level. This natural amount of oxygenated air, even with hyperventilation-type breathing, is unlikely to cause much harm.

This is not to be confused with breathing air with unnaturally high or manipulated percentages of oxygen. Just like balanced food diets, oxygen must also be taken in moderation. Too much oxygen causes oxidative stress, is toxic, and leads to cell death (Cooper et al. 2022; Koch et al. 2008). I would go so far as to argue that doctors who administer more than the 21 percent oxygen found at sea level are causing new and different issues by means of oxidative stress to the patients that they are trying to help. Specifically, the lungs and central nervous system are at risk of irreversible damage if exposed to pure oxygen for too long a period of time -- eventually leading to death.

Just the right amount of oxygen: Since our mammalian bodies are so well evolved, there is a wide range between too much and too little oxygen when it is naturally available at livable elevations. The problem is that in our sedentary lifestyles of this day and age, we do not breathe properly. A typical adult's regular inhale is short and quick. Although these typical inhales keep you alive, you are not using your lungs, your diaphragm, your blood vessels, and your heart sufficiently. The result of this poor breathing habit is insufficient oxygen -- not insufficient to live, but rather, insufficient to live well.

Deep breathing

Breathing is important. You have likely heard recommendations about and the benefits of yoga and breathing. But what about it is really so important? After all, we have all been breathing since birth.

I once injured my leg and was unable to jog for several weeks. When my leg recovered, I was extremely disappointed with my first jog. My lungs felt like they were going to explode. After a couple of weeks, I was back to normal. Unfortunately, about a year later, I injured my other leg in a similar manner. I knew that my downtime would be several weeks again, but I was determined not to have the same exploding-lung feeling when I returned to exercise. However, it was difficult to find something as good as jogging to get my muscles to work that hard. I thought hard about what it was that joggers did. Here is what I came up with.

Joggers lean forward until they start to fall. Then, they jump with one leg and catch themselves with the other -- and repeat. The repetition of the one-legged jump requires more use of large muscle groups which subsequently requires more blood flow to deliver more oxygen. This is accomplished by an elevated heart and breathing rate. And then it hit me. I remembered my lungs feeling like they were about to explode. Since I could barely walk or cycle and there was no convenient pool nearby, I decided to experiment with my lungs and ignore the heart rate. For six weeks, I breathed deeply every day for the same amount of time that I would have run had I not been injured. That is, I breathed in as deeply as I could -- to capacity, which required me to sit upright to get more air into my lungs -- before exhaling. After those six weeks, I ran -- not jogged. I was truly amazed. Yes, my leg muscles were sore for two days from six weeks of relative inactivity, but my lungs felt like they had not missed a beat. My heart rate recovery time was also poor, but my distance and time did not suffer anywhere close to what it had suffered after my first injury.

Eustress #3: Daily controlled oxygen deprivation

Keeping the deep breathing in mind, let us now introduce the eustress of controlled oxygen deprivation. The average adult breathes 12 to 16 breaths per minute. Each inhale is approximately equal in duration to the subsequent exhale during that average minute. What if you changed that? Here is my 10-level set of breathing exercises.

Level 1: Inhale-3, Exhale-3

For example, if you are trying to relax, catch your breath, or prepare for sleep, consider inhaling deeply for a count of three. The inhale will always be a full, deep breath. That count can be three "Mississippi's", three heartbeats, three ticks of a grandfather clock, three paces, or whatever seems appropriate to you at the time for the duration of this breathing exercise. The key is to breathe so deeply that you feel yourself fill both your belly and lungs. Although the air does not enter your belly, it is just a way of helping you to fully use your diaphragm -- the cross-sectional dome-shaped muscle that flexes to draw air into your lungs.

A strong recommendation here is to count:

One-Live-Love-Laugh-Learn,
Two-Live-Love-Laugh-Learn,
Three-Live-Love-Laugh-Learn,
...

Then, breathe out for the same count of three. Repeat this for 10 or 20 full deep breath cycles. The possible difficulty of saying "Live-Love-Laugh-Learn" repeatedly will slow you down, so do not rush it.

Level 2: Inhale-3, Exhale-4

Then, immediately afterwards, continue with a deep inhale for another count of three. But, this time, exhale for a count of four. Repeat this for another 10 or 20 repetitions.

Level 3: Inhale-3, Exhale-5

Next, continue with the same deep inhale for a three count, but exhale for a count of five. Repeat this for another 10 or 20 repetitions.

Realize that at this point you are only breathing in 3/8ths of the time now. That is 37.5 percent of the time versus the average breath cycle of 50 percent of the time.

You might find that you run out of air to exhale nearing the five count. If so, make sure that your count-of-three inhale is always as complete and deep as possible for the entire count of three. Then, control your exhale so that it does last for a full count of five.

Level 4: Inhale-3, Exhale-5, Hold(empty)-1

Once you are able to do the five-count exhales for 10 or 20 breath cycles, take it a step further by holding yourself (your lungs) empty for a count of one following the five-count exhale. That simply means neither inhaling nor exhaling for that one count.

To recap, you have progressed as follows:

- Inhale-3, Exhale-3: 10-20 times
- Inhale-3, Exhale-4: 10-20 times
- Inhale-3, Exhale-5: 10-20 times
- Inhale-3, Exhale-5, Hold(empty)-1: 10-20 times

Level 5: Inhale-3, Hold(full)-1, Exhale-5, Hold(empty)-1

For the next level, add a count of one while holding your breath in before exhaling. This has the added benefit of a bit of a lung stretch, especially if you are doing something active and bouncing. To be more specific, your inhalations should be active and strong in an attempt to quickly fill your lungs and continually stretch their capacity. This will help to improve your tidal volume -- the amount of air your lungs can inhale. The controlled slow exhale, on the other hand, should be passive or even limiting -- where you feel like you do not have enough air to expel -- yet relaxing. The only way to actively force your breath out is to engage either your abdominal muscles, chest muscles, or both. However, if you simply relax, you will naturally exhale sufficiently without effort. The effect is quite relaxing. Just try not to lose your posture on the exhales.

In a relatively short span of time, you will find that you can build up to:

Level 8: Inhale-3, Hold(full)-1, Exhale-5, Hold(empty)-4

On level 6 and 7, simply increase the count for holding yourself out to 2 and 3, respectively. By Level 8, you are holding yourself empty for 4 counts. This works out to inhaling for 3/13ths of the time by this point. That is inhaling for only 23.1 percent of your breath cycle -- less than half of the typical adult breath cycle. For over 69 percent of that breath cycle you will be either expelling air or holding yourself empty. This is putting eustress on your body and will encourage it to figure out how to use the oxygen it does receive more effectively.

Just use it

How often should you practice this? As often as possible.

Use it to get to sleep. Use it to wake up. Use it when you exercise. Use it when you are hungry. Use it when you are thirsty. Use it while you are getting a massage. Use it when you are cold. Use it when you feel overheated. Use it when you are triggered by an unwanted habit or reaction.

Just use it.

When this breathing exercise is no longer a challenge, take it up a notch by using this form of relaxation while you are doing repetitive exercises like jogging, skipping, or bouncing on a rebounder trampoline. Your body will then have to further fine tune its oxygen efficiency with higher demands from the active muscles.

Although deep breathing with exercise takes some getting used to, it is not as hard as it might sound. For a jogging example, inhale for three paces. Exhale for five paces. And, yes, build up to holding yourself empty for four paces -- on level 8. On a flat and consistent jog, it might take 5 to 10 minutes to build up to "inhale-3, hold(full)-1, exhale-5, hold(empty)-4". That is around one or two minutes of breathing multiplied by each of the incrementing eight levels. It takes a bit of concentration to maintain focus. You will find a rhythm and will then require focus to switch to the next level. Be patient with yourself. Remember, you will have reduced your oxygen inhale to 23.1% of the average time.

Since a slower pace will allow you to breathe in more deeply and vice versa, you will find that your jogging or activity speed will be controlled by your breath now.

"Control your breath, Control your life."

The nose

The simple task of breathing through the nose is a mammal's primary method of breathing. Mammals are obligate nasal breathers. But that does not mean that they all have to breathe through their nose. It just means that it is their typical preference (although some mammals, like horses, are obligate nasal breathers that cannot breathe through their mouths). The mammals that do have a choice typically only mouth breathe or breathe orally when they are very hot, very distressed, or have a diseased nasal cavity. This is thought to be an evolutionary trait for being able to continually smell the environment -- even while eating (chewing -- not while swallowing).

In 1981, experiments were conducted on monkeys by plugging their nostrils with silicone. Over time, their compensation by oral breathing noticeably altered not just their health but also their facial bone structure (Harvold et al. 1981).

Somehow, most humans have defaulted to breathing through their mouths instead -- the shortcut. The Cleveland Clinic agrees that humans are designed to breathe through their noses from birth (Cleveland Clinic, Nov 2020). The fact that most modern-day humans breathe orally may be related to the large number of chronic sinusitis cases worldwide. In 2018, the Centers for Disease Control (CDC) published that 28.9 million people in the U.S. were diagnosed with sinusitis. That is 11.6 percent of adults. Functional endoscopic sinus surgery (FESS) is used on 250,000 of those with sinusitis in the U.S. annually (CDC 2018).

Breathing orally by default has also been hypothesized as a link to common orthodontic and dental issues. Some of these issues include cramming of the teeth, where a tooth does not have room to come in. This type of cramming of the teeth affects 20 percent of people today (Pinhasi et al. 2015).

Pierre Robin, a Parisian stomatologist during the early 1900s, forced patients' upper palates to grow outward. In a few weeks, the patients' mouths grew larger which significantly improved their breathing (Robin 1934). For about 20 years, similar devices were created and used and a side benefit was found. Increased mouth size allowed for crooked teeth to straighten (Aggarwal et al. 2016). Similarly, as discussed in Chapter 7 on movement, even elderly people have had success in the reshaping of their facial bones by changing to nasal breathing in addition to other tongue and chewing habit changes (Mew 2004).

Level 9

Your lungs, although very hardy, work more effectively when the air they receive is of a specific temperature and humidity. When you breathe through your nose, the air is forced to circle through your intricately designed nasal cavities. The surface area that the inhaled air passes over is significantly larger when it passes through your nose than when you shortcut the inhale through your mouth. This additional nose-breathing surface area allows the air to be warmed and humidified, which further improves the lungs' efficiency in extracting oxygen. Therefore, you breathe more efficiently through your nose than you would if you inhaled through your mouth because your lungs can extract more oxygen from a given breath of air. As an added benefit, you have nose hairs that allow the air you breathe through your nose to filter out particles (Cleveland Clinic, Dec 2020). This can help reduce the risk of the spread of some diseases like the common cold.

Another benefit of nose breathing is that you are restricting the flow of air. Forcing your breath cycles through your nasal passages to humidify and warm the air requires additional force. On inhalation, that force is provided by your diaphragm. Nose breathing gives your diaphragm resistance. It is as if you are weight training your diaphragm. This is a very powerful exercise for you to get good at.

We do not stop at Level 8. To further limit your breath, practice the same oxygen deprivation progression of breathing but only through the nose for both inhales and exhales. Keep your lips sealed. You do not have to wait until you are exercising at Level 8 style breathing. Start breathing through your nose from the start if you can. Try to implement nasal breathing in your everyday breathing all the time.

Individual nostrils

Alternate nostril breathing is a yogic breath control practice. In Sanskrit it is referred to as "nadi shodhana pranayama". This approximately translates to "subtle energy-clearing breathing technique".

Although yoga can be a wonderful practice, that is not my goal here. Maybe you can relate to my thoughts on nostril breathing. I used to get annoyed when lying in bed with one nostril stuffed up. I would roll to the other side until it was clear for some relief, but it would inevitably plug the other nostril. It seemed like I was forever flipping myself like a pancake until I eventually fell asleep. This inspired me to solve the issue. Unfortunately, I do not think I did because it was due to either allergies or the common cold. But I did learn some interesting things. First, if I raised my upper back and head with pillows and lay on my back, the congestion almost always went away -- so maybe I did figure it out. However, I noticed that some slight congestion still shifted back and forth between nostrils. When I focused on this issue when I was not congested, ill, or suffering from allergies, I noted the same type of alternation, where one nostril always seemed to be subtly more open than the other. This was more pronounced while I was lying down. The first time I noticed, the nostril switching was on about a 30 minute switch cycle. This is what first prompted me to intervene and breathe through one nostril -- the more congested one -- in an attempt to alter the pattern. In doing so, I noticed that I had to remain calm because the air flow was a little more restricted, thereby working my diaphragm. When the breathing became easy, I switched to the other nostril and repeated.

On researching this, I discovered that it is a known phenomenon called the nasal cycle and papers have been written on it as early as 1895 -- maybe earlier (Kayser 1895).

Level 10

I have since made a regular resting practice out of encouraging an alternating nasal-cycle of breathing. I do my Level 8 oxygen deprivation breathing, but I cycle the inhale through my left nostril by closing my right nostril with a finger or knuckle. Then, exhale through the right while holding the left nostril closed. Then inhale from the right nostril and exhale through the left. This is done for the same counts as in Level 8 discussed above. At first, I did this because I wanted to control my own nasal cycle, but now I do it because I enjoy further restricting my breathing passage, thereby further strengthening my diaphragm -- more weight training for that muscle.

Freedivers

Freediving is a fascinating sport that also teaches some intricacies of breathing. For example, we spoke of "too much oxygen" above, but many freedivers have developed a method of breathing that they claim allows them to super-oxygenate their blood. They typically do not use unnatural or manipulated oxygen levels though. When freediving in the ocean, they have the benefit of some of the highest naturally existing percentage of oxygen on earth because they are at sea level. Over time and with practice, they train their blood cells to hold more oxygen by eustressing the body into producing more hemoglobin in their blood cells.

At sea level, there is about 20.9 percent oxygen in the air. When we breathe out a standard breath, it still has about 16.4 percent oxygen. If you were able to hold your breath for 3.5 minutes, your breath would still have around 7 percent oxygen left in it. Basically, humans are not very efficient at extracting oxygen from the air -- not when compared to a fish in water anyway. A fish has to extract about 7 mg/liter (7 ppm or 0.0007 percent) of oxygen out of sea water.

After this type of breathing, with an average sized breath left in the lungs (neither over-inflated lungs nor holding empty), the freediver can take advantage of this super-oxygenation and also has an extra average-sized breath on reserve. They typically will not take a last deep inhale -- just a regular inhale instead -- because it takes more muscle energy to hold it in. Also, their buoyancy is too high with a full, deep inhale.

Side note: The reflex that makes us want to inhale is not caused by the lack of oxygen in our lungs. Instead, it is the building percentage of carbon dioxide in our blood that gives us the urge to breathe. There are conflicting theories that hint that freedivers' breathing exercises allow for more effective removal of carbon dioxide from the body versus super-oxygenating. Regardless of which is correct, the freediver requires deep breathing for enough time that the majority of the body's blood can either super-oxygenate or be rid of as much carbon dioxide as possible.

This kundalini-style of breathing called *tummo* is not that relaxing though. If you want to prepare yourself for a physical feat, super-oxygenating your body can give you a caffeine-like boost. But, just like balanced food diets, oxygen must also be taken in moderation, so this type of breathing should be used sparingly.

To experiment with this, be sure to do this in a sitting or lying position and not while driving, in water, or anywhere where fainting might cause you harm. As a test, using a stopwatch, just take a breath and time how long you can hold your breath without any special breathing preparation. Actual seconds versus counting or heartbeats is preferred here since your heart rate will likely soon adjust its speed. Note the time.

Then, in a sitting or lying position, inhale for a count of three and immediately relax your chest and abdomen while allowing yourself to exhale without force for a count of one. Ideally, both inhale and exhale are done through your nose only. Do not force the air out in that count of one. Just follow it directly with your next three-count inhale. You will likely feel lightheaded. Repeat this for three full minutes.

After three minutes, inhale a regular breath (not so deep a breath that you waste energy while trying to hold it in), start the timer, hold your breath, and relax. Avoid looking at the stopwatch. The length of time you can hold your breath may noticeably have improved after just one attempt. Feel free to do the entire process a few more times.

With practice, and only after you know how your body reacts to it, this breathing cycle can be incorporated into movement exercises for short periods of time. For example, on a jog, if you see a hill coming, you can alter your breath this way. The difference is that you will not be testing yourself by holding your breath. Instead, you will be running up the impending hill. You will effectively super-oxygenate your blood in advance when you see the hill in the distance -- ideally about three minutes before, if possible. Then, you will be able to make it up the hill more efficiently. Once at the top, you will want to start transitioning back to the Level 8 relaxed breathing.

Remember that the eustress (holding your breath or running up a hill) is necessary to build up the body. Simply super-oxygenating your blood will not encourage more hemoglobin production or the release of neurotransmitters. The eustress of running out of oxygen and allowing your body to deal with carbon dioxide snaps the body into an emergency performance mode.

Holding yourself empty: There is another interesting eustress breath-hold challenge for which you also do not need to take up freediving. The safest way to implement this is in the comfort of your own home. Even better, from a sitting or lying position. Once you are comfortable with how your body responds, you can do it while walking or during other light exercise. You should not lose consciousness when doing this, but always plan for the possibility that you might. This should help keep you safe. Always perform breath-holding exercises with great caution. If you are walking or doing some other sort of light exercise while holding your breath and start to feel faint, kneel, sit, or lie down immediately and breathe normally. This is an indication that you have pushed too far, too fast. Be patient with your body. Give yourself time to adjust and build. The breath hold itself can be done either as you would expect -- after the inhale -- or, for more of a challenge, after the exhale. Holding yourself (your lungs) empty after the exhale does not give the body as much of a reserve to use. Only the oxygen already in the blood will be available. This eustress can have a quick, full-body effect. When it comes to oxygen deprivation, the body has no choice but to react more quickly.

Consider experimenting with different breathing cycles for at least three minutes each. Follow each breathing cycle with a breath hold of your choice (after the inhale or the exhale). Judge your progress by recording the times. This is a very uncomfortable exercise if you have not done it before, but do not use anything other than your own willpower to hold your breath. It can even seem painful. Some freedivers have said that the initial discomfort can be pushed through. I find that a relaxed mind gets me the farthest. Once you restart your breathing, return to the same breathing cycle you chose to explore for another minimum of three minutes. Now, repeat the exercise again at least three to ten times. You will likely notice an improvement even on your first few sets. When your performance starts to decrease in the same session, you have likely come to the natural conclusion of that session for that sitting. Experimenting on breathing cycles and breath-hold methods helps you to learn about yourself. Experiment often with great curiosity, but safety must always be the first priority.

Three types of oxygen deprivation summarized

If you find that it is challenging to combine these breathing techniques with activity, consider that you might not yet have trained your breath as well as you have trained your muscles for that activity. For example, let us say you can run a 10-minute mile for five minutes, but you have plateaued there in your attempts to become faster or run that speed longer. Then, you build to "Inhale-3, Hold(full)-1, Exhale-5, Hold(empty)-4", yet you find that you now run more slowly -- maybe an 11-minute mile -- for those five minutes. I would venture that, with a few more practice runs, you will find that you might temporarily run an 11-minute mile, but it will be for longer than five minutes. Then, build to 10 minutes of running at the 11-minute mile pace. Once you have broken that five minute limitation by a significant amount, you can revisit the speed. These intentionally applied eustresses can be used for their neurotransmitter-emitting benefits, or they can be used to help you to break your perceived limitations (habits).

The main point is that, while merely sitting, anybody can quickly and easily experiment with the eustress of controlled oxygen deprivation. The first type described here -- which should be used often -- was the reduction of the duration of inhalations in a relaxed breath cycle. The second -- which should be used sparingly -- was to super-oxygenate your body before enduring an activity that might require more oxygen than generally expected for a short period. The third was to hold yourself empty after an exhale between a minimum of three minute breath cycles.

Even light experimentation with these will elicit noticeable effects in your mind and with your body. With curiosity and by regularly repeating this eustress, you will improve your body.

However, avoid breathing in these ways with the hope or goal that it will become natural to you. Rather, consider the benefits of setting the goal to breathe mindfully for large portions of your ordinary day. This more active mentality will make your breathing exercises more purposeful.

Breathing may seem trivial because you have literally breathed your entire life, but even your breathing is likely to have developed into an unwanted habit in need of fixing. Deep breathing exercises can be done anywhere and at any time. They can be done sitting or standing, with your eyes open or closed. You can do them while lying down or exercising. Just take a few minutes out of your day to focus on your breath and let go of everything else you might be thinking about at the same time, if possible. If you feel like you cannot spare a few minutes, how about just a few seconds -- a few breaths?

CHAPTER 10

HYDRATION

"Thousands have lived without love, not one without water." (W. H. Auden)

Water deprivation can be used to proactively inflict eustress on ourselves. Limiting your water intake in a controlled fashion is a middle ground between fasting and oxygen deprivation.

Review on eating: A healthy human body can tolerate weeks without food and not sustain permanent damage. The eustress proposed in Chapter 8 was a single full day of fasting -- from after the previous day's dinner until the following day's breakfast -- about 35 hours -- repeated once per week.

Review on oxygen: A healthy human body can only tolerate minutes without oxygen before experiencing permanent damage. The eustress proposed in Chapter 9 lasted just a few seconds, yet less than half of the oxygen was inhaled over each breathing cycle.

We need water: In the middle, between eating and breathing, a healthy human body can tolerate a few days without water.

Water ranks high on the human necessity scale, somewhere between food and oxygen. We know it is essential for physical and psychological functioning. It is significant that about 60 percent of an average adult body is water. Beyond its dominant position in our body composition, water is a crucial need for every cell, tissue, and organ in the human body. For example, our blood uses water to carry nutrients and oxygen to cells. It is similarly used to flush toxins from the body, regulate body temperature, protect our organs and tissues, lubricate and cushion joints, and so much more. This is the key reason humans cannot do without it.

Mahatma Gandhi skipped eating for protracted periods, but he certainly had water throughout. It is impossible to imagine going for weeks without water, just as no one has lived a day without oxygen. However, Muslims who practice fasting during Ramadan are not permitted to drink water between sunrise and sunset. This can work out to 10 to 19 hours at a stretch, depending on where on the planet they are located. The temperature can also be above 100 degrees Fahrenheit (40 degrees Celsius) during the Ramadan fasting period. Despite this, people often feel that it is inconceivable for anyone to be expected to function properly without a constant supply of water. Such people usually think in extremes.

At one extreme, clinical dehydration can cause fatigue, muscle cramps, and headaches. If left unattended, dehydration becomes severe and may lead to serious health problems such as heat stroke and kidney failure. At the other extreme, too much water can fill up your stomach at a rate that exceeds your ability to process it until it overflows into your lungs -- drowning. A little less extreme, hyponatremia is a condition in which the level of sodium in the blood is abnormally low as a percentage of the amount of fluid it is dissolved in. Sodium is an electrolyte that helps maintain inter- and intracellular fluid levels. Cell swelling as a result of low sodium levels can lead to seizures, coma, and sometimes, death. The middle ground lies between dehydration and drowning.

Crippled by these natural limitations, people instinctively believe their water intake should never be restricted. They consume as many liters of water as their time and natural inclination allow. They are further motivated by organizations like the U.S. National Academies of Sciences, Engineering, and Medicine publishing that the recommended daily fluid intake is 15.5 cups (125 ounces or 3.7 liters) of fluids per day for men and about 11.2 cups (91 ounces or 2.7 liters) of fluids per day for women. I am not challenging these numbers. I am only challenging the idea that these fluids need to be trickled constantly into your mouth throughout the day.

With so many proponents of the philosophy that water should be drunk as much as possible, it seems absurd that anyone would try to cut their water intake. However, I will not be asking you to cut your daily intake. I am challenging you to build up a resistance to sipping it all day long every time you feel thirst. To do this, you will have to drink a bit more water when it is available. At the same time, you must be sure not to overdo things in the other direction.

Like several other elements discussed in this book, how much fluid you need per day is largely personal. It depends on your body size, your age, what you did in the last few hours, if you are recovering from anything, the temperature, what you ate recently, your activity level, and many other possible factors. Therefore, published numbers are just averages for whatever sample size researchers used.

Eustress #4: Daily controlled water deprivation

Before our ancient ancestors learned how to make water-retaining vessels, they had to make it to the next creek, stream, river, or lake in order to rehydrate. I propose that you re-teach your body how to withstand the equivalent of a trip between water sources rather than carrying it with you everywhere and all the time.

The eustress proposed here is to accomplish full movement exercises or to spend a few hours of every day without water. In preparation for movement exercises (regardless of their intensity or duration), a long day, or activities in dry or hot climates, ensure you are well- but not over-hydrated beforehand. Then, simply abstain from so much as sipping water during and immediately after the activity. The activity depends on your practice and comfort level. In the beginning, you might just not sip water on a short jog. Then, maybe, you build the jog up to 10 kilometers. Then, after sufficient time to learn how your body responds, you will go for longer without water -- even for full-day hikes. However, I do recommend that you always carry water for emergencies -- just battle the urge to sip it. Once you have practiced this, you will be amazed at how much more focused you can be without the thought of needing a water break.

Though you will feel thirst and a desire to drink when it is hot and you are exercising, you will not cause yourself harm. Over their 10 to 19 hour daily fasts during Ramadan, Muslims have not been seen to have any ill effects or signs of dehydration (Leiper et al. 2003). Even with vigorous activity like full daytime rugby matches where fluids were only consumed before sunrise and after sunset, dehydration was not indicated (Trabelsi et al. 2011).

During a single vigorous workout, you can sweat and evaporate 34 fl. oz (1 liter) of water. That equates to about 2.2 pounds (1kg) in weight. Although this might sound like a lot, the effect on your body is based on your practiced tolerance. This is something that you will slowly build up. Do not attempt a full marathon for the first time without drinking water. However, this is possible with time, practice, mental preparation, and attention to your body. However, I am not recommending anything that extreme here. It takes much less effort than that to accomplish the controlled water deprivation proposed here.

Think about your typical exercise routine and watch others. Weight lifters will feel the need for sips of water between sets. Tennis players feel the need for water between every game of a set. Even just driving around town on a warm day might make you feel the need for water. It all comes down to balance. Your body can and does hold a lot of water. You do not require an intravenous drip of liquid to keep your body hydrated all day. Unless you are an extreme athlete performing at your peak, your water consumption can be taken well before or well after activity. But do not misunderstand. You will need to ensure that you have had enough to drink each day. I am just challenging you to build up to not feeling the need to have it spread out over your day at the first sign of thirst. On the other hand, the idea is to not drink like a camel in a single sitting. There is a happy medium in between. You just have to find yours. Everybody is different. There is no hard-and-fast rule to knowing your limits.

To further make this manageable, be sure to include the lesson from Chapter 9 on nasal breathing. Breathing through your mouth will allow a large amount of water to be with your breath released as humidity. Nasal breathing forces the air through evolutionarily designed nasal passages to perfectly swirl the air past an optimal number of nasal respiratory epithelial cells that will do their best to grab as much of that humidity as they can so as not to waste it.

Many people who do strenuous activities will experience a "cotton mouth" feeling from feeling parched. Nasal breathing will help prevent that. If you try but still feel parched, practice the exercise with a small mouthful of water without swallowing for long periods of time -- even hours. As far back as the Spartans and Genghis Khan, the ability for warriors to be able to run up a mountain with just a mouthful of water was reportedly considered a sign of a disciplined and well-trained body, accustomed to both oxygen and water deprivation. They were expected to spit out the same mouthful of water when they had completed the run back to the bottom. Therefore, it should be reasonable to assume that your daily jog, tennis match, martial arts class, football period, bike ride, or whatever your activity is, can be endured without a sip of water.

When you challenge your body in healthy ways, the eustress

you create triggers your central nervous system to respond. Due to a chronic lack of use, our bodies have withheld these beneficial responses. Along with these natural and healthy responses come mammalian superpowers that allowed our ancient ancestors to survive and thrive. It would behoove us to take advantage of these built-in gifts because they are within each of us, just waiting to be called on.

CHAPTER II

MASSAGE

"When the mind suffers, the body cries out."
(Cardinal Lamberto -- The Godfather Part III)

After mentally challenging a lifetime of unwanted habits, moving your body in ways that you have not done since childhood, depriving your body of food, oxygen, and water, it is important to remember to be kind to yourself. Spoil yourself. Pamper yourself. But you can also do much good with uncomfortable comforts.

Massage is a natural, hands-on therapy that uses pressure and strokes the body to relieve pain and tension. It is centered on the use of touch to manipulate the soft tissues of the body and promote relaxation, relieve pain, or improve fluid circulation. It is considered alternative medicine and it complements other therapies and medical treatments very well. This form of therapy has been used for centuries to help people relax and heal.

Your body is constantly creating new cells and getting rid of old, damaged ones. This process of cell turnover is essential for keeping your body healthy and functioning properly. However, sometimes this process can become slow or sluggish, causing cellular waste to build up in your body. This build up can be due to regular use and healthy exercise, due to trauma or distress, or can be caused by a sedentary lifestyle. Whatever the cause, it can lead to a variety of health problems including fatigue, muscle aches, skin problems, and various forms of inflammation. Massage helps to speed up the process of cell turnover and cellular waste removal by forcing increased blood flow and lymphatic drainage.

Both mind and body tension as well as pain can be aided by therapeutic massage. Empirical studies have shown that massage improves circulation and increases flexibility and range of motion while significantly reducing fatigue. It all depends on the type of massage therapy and the quality of the therapist.

Types

Many people have an image of what a massage is based on movies, reputation, or experience. The most typical seems to be the relaxing spa-type massage. However, there is much more to massage than meets the eye. There are so many types of massage to choose from that it can be very overwhelming. Different types of massage pressure can be used to achieve different results. Here is a brief overview of the most popular styles:

Swedish massage is the modality that comes to mind when most people think about massage. It is a soft tissue massage that uses long, smooth strokes to promote relaxation. It is a light massage. This is the most common type offered in clinics and spas, and it is beneficial for increasing circulation. It is typically performed with calming music and scented oils.

Hot stone massage involves the use of smooth, heated stones. The therapist places the stones on specific points on your body. Then, they massage your body with the stones using long, gliding strokes. The heat from the stones helps to relax your muscles and ease any tension or pain you may feel. The therapist may also use cold stones during your massage to help reduce inflammation.

Sports massage was specifically designed to help athletes in training and competition. It is the massage type you would seek to maintain peak performance and injury prevention. Sports massage can be used before, during, and after athletic events. It aims to improve circulation, increase range of motion, and therefore injury prevention.

Shiatsu is a traditional form of Japanese massage that uses pressure and finger strokes on the body. It is said to help improve circulation and promote relaxation. Shiatsu has been used for healing in Asia for centuries.

Reflexology is based on the principle that key points in the hands and feet correspond to meridians of the body. By applying pressure to these points, it is possible to promote healing and relaxation in the corresponding areas of the body.

Thai massage involves stretching and deep pressure along the body's energy lines, where the practitioner often uses their full body weight and whole-body movements. It improves flexibility, circulation, and mental well-being.

Deep tissue massage is intended to be intense and is used for therapeutic purposes. A therapist uses slow strokes and firm pressure often to reach your inner -- less superficial -- muscle layers. They may also use techniques such as myofascial release to break up any scar tissue or adhesions in the area being treated. This can help reduce pain and increase the range of motion by realigning deeper layers of muscles and connective tissue.

Trigger point massage focuses on specific areas of the body that are known to cause pain. These areas -- trigger points -- usually present themselves as knots and are usually located in the muscles themselves. They can be caused by a variety of reasons such as repetitive movements, poor posture, or distress. A trigger point massage aims to break down the knots in the muscle tissue. This will release the muscle to improve range of motion, flexibility, and many other blocking issues. This entails firm pressure points to release the muscle tension.

Eustress #5: Semi-monthly forced muscle manipulation

Most limitations are often caused by circumstances motivated by an individual's actions, inactions, or habits. Though these limitations may have been initiated by external circumstances which may have occurred years prior, your current responses are mostly habits internal to your body and mind. The Lebanese-American writer Khalil Gibran wrote, "Your living is determined not so much by what life brings to you as by the attitude you bring to life; not so much by what happens to you as by the way your mind looks at what happens" (Gibran, ~1925). In other words, you cannot control what led you to your current situation. It is in the past. But what you do next is your choice.

Just as we talked about the need for movement, the movement

itself generates cellular waste products. These waste products can also build up from lack of use, lack of blood flow, and a sedentary lifestyle. They often need help to be filtered out and flushed from your system. This is especially true when we do things that you are not used to -- in this case, choosing eustress. If you push yourself healthily, you can get sore muscles in the beginning. This is expected and encouraged, but we also need to encourage the filtering and flushing.

In the ancient martial art of Kalaripayattu, the teacher would deep massage his students before training. This was not done to relax them. In fact, it was not relaxing at all. It was done daily for weeks in a row if necessary. This massage was more like a Thai massage, in that the teacher would use whatever means necessary to remove the knots of the muscles and expose underlying injuries if they existed. If the student was able to withstand the pain and the teacher was pleased with their lack of injuries, training would begin. This type of massage had the added benefit of improving flexibility, but the first few days would be very painful as it takes time for the cell waste to be filtered out of the body.

I once attempted to mimic this as best I could with 30 consecutive days of Thai massage. Admittedly, I did have to skip days two, three, five, and seven, and I distinctly remember being in a lot of pain on day eight's massage. But I did survive the last 23 consecutive days. In the end, there was one knot that could not be resolved. Aside from that and after a couple of days of rest after the last massage, I felt like a new person. I do not believe that my muscles have felt that great since then.

This is an extreme that you do not need to go to. My point is that you choose what you feel you want and need. But I do recommend a minimum of 90 minutes of massage a minimum of once a month. Twice a month is better. Once per week would be fantastic. Unfortunately, cost might be the inhibiting factor (though the cost will be worth every penny), unless you marry a massage therapist who is willing to bring work home.

The type of massage should not be a relaxing, simple effleurage, light rubbing, feel-good type of massage. I recommend that you find the strongest, heaviest, most forceful -- yet professional, registered, and certified -- massage therapist that you can build up a relationship with. Your muscles -- even your injured ones after a week or so post-injury -- are very durable. If you are not sore, do not worry. Get a massage anyway. You should be at least a little sore the day after a good massage when you are not accustomed to them. A good massage therapist that has had time to get to know your body can push the boundaries of your muscles right up to your tolerance range. As they find and dance the fine line of your tolerance range, a good trick is to breathe through what might feel like a bad pain. A good massage therapist will pulse their force along with your breathing rhythm. They will guide you when to inhale deeply and when to exhale. It is a great opportunity to utilize the breathing exercises discussed in Chapter 9.

Ask your massage therapist to use deep tissue techniques with as much force as they can sustain. They will be hesitant at first, but as you build a relationship with them, they will learn that you are trying to eustress your body repeatedly over time. You are trying to squeeze out stagnant waste that has not moved as a result of your sedentary lifestyle or fresh lactic acid from active muscles. Once they learn that you are a regular client, they will see that you are serious and are willing to build up a tolerance to the pain for the good of your health and body. You are aiming to have muscles you did not know you had massaged and worked. Your lymphatic system will be stimulated to drain in the massage process, and circulation to it will be encouraged. Have a full body massage for about an hour with an additional 20 to 30 minutes dedicated to one concise area -- ideally totaling 90 minutes. Then, change the dedicated area every visit. The therapist should keep a record of what you had massaged and when. This is important because you will not be able to have focused and forceful massage done for your entire body all in one session. It is also physically demanding on the massage therapist and you want them to be in full control when they are at work, so 90 minutes should be the maximum.

The deep manipulation of the muscles improves circulation and releases lactic acid and other stagnant blockers. These things are released into the bloodstream so that your kidneys, liver, and other organs can process them for excretion from your body. If not done frequently enough, the initial feeling after a massage might make you feel nauseous, give you a headache, or make your muscles ache for a couple of days post-massage.

These should not be indications to have massages less often. Rather, book your next one immediately. Allow your body to become accustomed to dealing with the release of these waste products so that it becomes more efficient at expelling them. This, too, needs practice.

CHAPTER 12
CUPPING

"If there is free flow, there is no pain. If there is pain, there is no free flow." (Li Dong Yuan)

You have probably seen pictures or videos of people with large, circular bruises on their bodies. These bruises are the result of cupping, an ancient practice that is enjoying a resurgence in popularity. So what is cupping?

A brief history of cupping

Cupping (or vacuum cupping) is the anglicized name for a technique that has been used for centuries in traditional Chinese medicine as well as in ancient Egyptian practices. It is also known as *hijama* in Arabic. The cupping discussed here is all about dry cupping. The alternative, wet cupping, involves skin lacerations so that blood is drawn by suction (Al-Bedah et al. 2019). Wet cupping is not discussed or recommended here.

The original process of dry cupping used bamboo, metal, or glass cups. The therapist lit a small fire inside the cup to warm the air inside. As the flame died out, they quickly placed the cup against the skin in specific places. When the flame extinguished -- either by burning out or through a lack of oxygen -- the heated air inside cooled abruptly, which created a vacuum. This resulted in the skin being pulled up into the cup. When you do this, you may feel some discomfort as the skin is pulled from the underlying muscles. This pulling breaks up the fascia that tends to hold the skin in place due to injury, lack of movement or activity, inflammation, or trauma. The therapist will typically leave the cup in place for several minutes before relieving the pressure and removing it. Cupping this way will leave a circular mark on your skin where the cups were placed. These marks are harmless and usually go away within a week or two. They are the result of blood being drawn closer to the surface than usual. It is like a superficial bruise (Shmerling 2020). A bruise is the product of internal bleeding typically caused by inward pressure. Cupping has forced blood cells out of their vessels, but caused by an outward pressure. Cupping is basically like a hickey.

The separation of the skin from the muscle and subsequent breakdown of the fascia in between is said to help with pain, inflammation, and blood circulation, and to loosen or release muscles to promote healing (Aboushanab et al. 2018). It is also thought that cupping therapy draws out toxins and congestion from the body while improving and unblocking the flow of energy through the body's meridians. It can even be used to break apart certain types of scar tissue.

Modern cupping

Recall the photos of Michael Phelps' shoulders and back in the 2016 Olympic Games that included such suction marks. Similar marks can be seen on other celebrities as they research ways to more efficiently heal themselves.

Rather than using flame-generated vacuum, more modern cupping sets come with various types of pumps to generate the vacuum. These are generally safer since they do not require fire. They are also typically made of hard plastic. Even more recently, silicone ones have been produced. Some are self-pumping. Other high-end ones come complete with a built-in computer with choices on intensity and duration.

Another, newer cupping method involves lubricating a large skin area with massage oil -- typically following a muscle. A little less pressure is used in the cup. Then, the cup is slid slowly along the muscle's length. This picks up the skin and rolls it evenly over the length of the full muscle rather than in just one localized spot. The technique of sliding the cup in this way typically results in premature vacuum loss, so using a pump-style set makes it much easier to reapply the vacuum versus having to light a flame to do the same. Technology has its perks.

Eustress #6: Bi-monthly cupping

The eustress to apply here is to have a cupping therapy session at least once per month -- or, even better, twice per month. If you have never experienced it before, it is best to have cupping done professionally a few times. Inquire with your local acupuncturist, chiropractor, massage therapist, medical doctor, physical therapist, or naturopath that practices cupping therapy. A professional will allow you to experience how it is done. Do not be deterred by the marks they leave. Like massage, commit to at least three or four sessions before hastily judging whether it is for you or not.

Once you see how simple it is, learn key spots as well as where to not apply it, you can pick up a cupping kit for your own home use. The what-not-to-do's are pretty logical. Do not over-cup or repeat an area that you have already cupped. Also, do not cup over a wound, eyes, ears, orifices, nipples, or other weird ideas you might come up with. Just stick to the large muscle groups on your legs, arms, and back. You can find cupping sets in many places. Amazon sells decent sets between $20 and $50 (US dollars). My preference are the kits with a hand pump gun because they are inexpensive, reliable, and easy to clean.

CHAPTER 13

GOING BAREFOOT

"And forget not that the earth delights to feel your bare feetand the winds long to play with your hair."
(Khalil Gibran)

One of the simplest, most natural things a person can do is to avoid putting on socks, shoes, slippers, flip-flops, sandals, clogs, or other foot coverings. Of course, this might seem absurd for most of our active lives since society tends to frown upon going to the office barefoot. Many restaurants and stores still post "no shirts, no shoes, no service" warnings. A staggering number of people also worry that it is easy to get injured when you walk barefoot. This might be why some parents are overly encouraging their infants to walk in shoes when they are just learning to walk. Even fashion and marketing have done well at making people world-wide judge others by their shoes, styles, name brands, and colors. Due to this, most people do not even consider walking around barefoot as often as possible.

Real risks

Diseases: Technically, walking barefoot can expose your feet to a variety of diseases and infections, including hookworm, athlete's foot, warts, and others. Typically, however, these are found in unclean public and overpopulated areas like public pools and showers, baths, and change rooms. The floors in these places are typically flat and hard -- very unnatural. Aside from the diseases, it is not much different from walking around barefoot on hardwood or tile floors in your own home. Although freeing your feet from socks, shoes, and slippers at home allows your toes to spread out nicely, there is more to it than that. In public pools, change rooms, and the like, wear some kind of sandal, slipper, or flip flop to maintain good hygiene. It is not the terrain we are after anyway.

Wounds: Without shoes to protect your feet, you are definitely more likely to experience cuts, scrapes, thorns, bruises, and punctures if you walk on rough or sharp surfaces. There is no telling where splinters, glass shards, and other sharp or pointed objects are buried, hidden, or just unseen.

It is a catch-22 though. If you do not often walk barefoot, you will have tender feet -- literally a tenderfoot to barefoot walking. Due to your tender feet, you will be more susceptible to injury. However, if you walk barefoot often, your feet will develop calluses, be tougher, more durable, and will be less susceptible to injury over time. Of course, I doubt they would ever become durable enough to withstand glass shards or other hidden surprises, so consider your terrain wisely.

Burns: Hot pavements or rocks, hot sand, and even prolonged sun exposure can burn the soles of your feet. Oftentimes vacationers will head to a warm climate to spend time on a beach. They will wear shoes on their way to their relaxing towel or chair to protect their feet from the hot sand. But then, they take them off, rub down with protective sun cream, skip the soles of their feet, and lie belly down, risking sun burns on the soles of their feet. The soles of your feet can burn too. Look after them because they are your primary connection to the natural earth.

Bites: Sure, if you step on a bee or wasp while barefoot, you will get stung. But it is not like they were out to get you. They were being defensive and were trying to protect themselves. They likely died in the act, while you just got a sting. Snakes, dogs, cats, and other animals you might fear bites from are not going to try to bite the soles of your feet. If they want to harm you, they will likely bite your ankle or leg. Shoes are unlikely to make that much safer for you.

Injury: Stubbing your toe must be one of the most infuriating injuries. Most of the time the pain only lasts for a few minutes. But, in those few minutes, I have been in so much pain that I was certain I had broken a toe. I have actually broken toes and every time I was in less pain than when I typically stub my toe. There is no doubt that wearing shoes will decrease the possibility of your clumsy walking ending in a stubbed toe. But what was the situation when you stubbed your toe? Were you multitasking -- walking and checking your phone, thinking of something other than walking and not paying attention to where you were walking? The issue there might not be with walking shoeless.

Poor hygiene and aesthetics: There is little doubt that the look of dirty feet is less appealing than the look of clean feet. Going to bed with dirt-stained feet is not something I do or recommend. It is almost impossible for me to believe that someone can walk barefoot in their neighborhood without stepping on a bit of sloppily picked up or smeared dog feces. So wash your feet often.

Rewards

Walking barefoot is one of the most active activities anyone can engage in. It appears superficially simple, yet offers a host of benefits, from improving your posture to strengthening your muscles. A slow walk can become a full lower-body workout on the right (or wrong) terrain.

Ancient Egyptians figured out the benefits of foot massages over 4,000 years ago. But, somehow, only a few of us continue to practice it for ourselves in this day and age. If you cannot see yourself walking on natural, uneven, challenging terrain barefoot, consider booking regular appointments with a reflexologist to undo the stiff and limiting damage that your shoes have caused your feet. The art of reflexology involves the application of pressure to points on the feet (as well as hands and ears). This is done to counteract and even correct health issues, both mental and physical. The simple act of walking on natural, uneven ground has a similar ability to apply pressure and stimulate the nerve endings of the feet to those same pressure points without you even having to think about it -- like a proactive reflexology session just by walking.

Walking barefoot will improve your balance, posture, and flexibility. It will also force you to walk more carefully, thereby not relying on a thick and falsely over-padded heel-strike. Most people will walk with a heel strike when they walk quickly in shoes. But on uneven ground, that same stride would risk a potentially bruised heel from a piece of gravel. To compensate while barefoot, you will typically switch to a toe-striking gait (using the ball of our foot, actually). This changes your stride by allowing us not to commit fully to the step. You are able to either bounce back or to lower the heel in order to move your weight to a different part of the foot. Naturally, this may slow your pace down at first, but it also engages a few more shock-absorbing bones, joints, and muscles during your walk. So, with a heel-striking gait, the pounding of your walk goes from the heel, the lower leg's tibia and fibula bones, the knee, the upper leg's femur, the hip, and finally to your spine. On the other hand, a toe-strike gait will utilize your foot's metatarsal bones and ankle joint in addition to others. Your calf muscles will be used to absorb shock on landing with a toe strike, rather than just for a pushing off when using a heel strike. Using these additional joints and muscles will take a significant load off your knees, hips, and vertebrae, even when compared to using a shoe's thickly padded heel (Wallace et al. 2018).

When on uneven ground, your feet -- but, more specifically, your toes -- will work harder to grip the ground. Each toe will have to work independently rather than being buffered by a shoe. Every toe will have to hold its own weight. This will improve strength, balance, and proprioception.

Another benefit of walking barefoot is that it can help you connect with nature. Feeling grounded by the skin-to-earth feeling will help you become more aware of your surroundings and pay attention to the sensations under your feet.

Having fallen arches, flat feet, bunions, and issues like this are not good reasons to avoid walking barefoot. Rather, consider that they are likely the symptom of forcing your feet into unnatural shoes for a lifetime. Insoles potentially put unreasonable pressure on a tendon that is over-stressed, which may further limit blood flow and then slow the healing process. Although many shoes and insoles might allow us to walk or run post-injury, not allowing ourselves sufficient rest to fully heal from an injury is typically a more damning issue. If you were to keep up your foot tendon strength, injury may be altogether preventable in many cases.

Eustress #7: More time barefoot daily

I am not talking about switching to toe socks or "barefoot" shoes. When I say "barefoot", I mean just that -- the skin of the soles of your feet touching the natural earth.

At home: Consider no longer wearing shoes and socks in your home. At a minimum, this will allow your feet to breathe and your toes to splay out naturally. If you have smelly feet or shoes, you most certainly wear your shoes too much. That does not mean that you will not benefit from going barefoot if your feet and shoes do not stink, though. However, this is not the ideal natural earth terrain.

Grass: If you are still hesitating at the thought of spending more time barefoot, you can still start off in the comfort of your home. But hardwood, tile, and carpet are not rough or uneven surfaces. We are attempting to eustress your feet. If you have a garden, do your gardening barefoot. Parks can also be quite pleasurable to wander around barefoot. Grass is a wonderfully slow way to start to build up your foot tolerance to varying and irregular pressures.

Urban terrain: Build up your tolerance and duration. Start with simple barefoot walks around your house and property. Build up to walking barefoot around your block, then around the neighborhood. Build up to jogging barefoot.

Tougher and rougher: If I had to choose my barefoot eustress between shorter and rougher terrain versus flatter and longer exposure, I would push to build on the tougher and rougher terrain because it is so quick and easy to do. However, you should really be exposing yourself to both types of barefoot eustress.

Build up to walk on gravel driveways or beaches. If it is too difficult for you, just stand on the gravel. Aim to stand still for just one minute. Then take two steps to change the pressure points, stand still again, and repeat. If you do not have a gravel driveway or access to one nearby, make a frame on your patio or corner of your house, fill it with gravel from your local hardware or garden store, and just stand on it. Use marbles if you do not want to use gravel.

For flatter and longer exposure for a different style of barefoot eustress, go for a barefoot trail hike through the woods and forest. Build up how much of the hike you do barefoot. Go for short barefoot jogs around your neighborhood. Build up to longer jogs if you feel like you can do it without injury or excessive wear of the soles of your feet. This will also allow the soles of your feet to toughen up, allow your individual toe tendons to learn to hold their weight again, and remind your toes that they are allowed to work independently. If you are really afraid of being seen outside barefoot and have no way of getting gravel or marbles in an enclosed space indoors, consider the MELT (myofascial energetic length technique) with proper density balls.

The myofascial energetic length technique (MELT) is a bodywork therapy that uses slow, gentle strokes to release the myofascial tissue and restore balance in the body. It will stretch the tissues in your feet, releasing any restrictions and restoring free movement. Just remember to use proper density balls.

Rain, cold, or shine: Even if it is rainy or cold, continue the barefoot exposure. If dogs can walk through snow and ice without footwear, you can too. I am not recommending that you walk barefoot in the snow or ice, but if it is raining and cold (but above freezing), then absolutely do it! This is not supposed to be comfortable. It is supposed to be eustress that takes effort, time, and patience to build up. That said, it should not cause injury or distress. Just like exercise, fasting, and oxygen and water deprivation, do not make this too extreme too quickly. Be patient with your body if you are trying to *Fix Yourself*.

Look at your feet: Take your shoes and socks off right now and take a good look at the underside of your toes. Are they shaped like puzzle pieces – perfectly shaped to fit to your adjacent toes? Contrast them with your fingers which are rounded and typically do not leave signs of the adjacent fingers in the skin. The lack of independent use of individual toes, their lack of bending and feeling, pushing, and prodding is leaving them susceptible to a lack of blood flow and an accumulation of byproducts that our bodies were made to excrete. The lack of independent toe use causes some to disproportionately take on more or less weight than they have evolved to take on. It changes how you weight your feet, which in turn changes how you stand and walk. This changes how your bones grow and how they bend with repeated misuse. This, over time, causes more and more intense irregularities in your step, which translates into structural body issues. If you have inexplicable pains in an ankle, knee, hip, or back, my bet is that you have not spent enough time barefoot.

The buildup of calluses on the feet is a good thing. For the 200,000 years of our species' existence, they were our original, built-in shoes. Only in the last 40,000 years have we used foot coverings. But the thicker layer of naturally callused skin additionally protects us from heat, cold, and abrasion. This is typically counterintuitive in a popular culture that has us believing that foot calluses are a negative thing and the soft-to-the-touch sole a positive one. Another mistaken belief is that thicker calluses equal less sensitivity. Nicholas Holowka of Harvard University along with a team of researchers from the U.S., Germany, and Kenya have found that the repetition of barefoot activities that lead to foot callus buildup does not decrease the overall sensitivity of the foot (Holowka et al. 2019). Therefore, thicker calluses will be more likely to protect you from injury or pain from a stone, but you will still feel its presence.

If you are concerned about having non-aesthetically rough feet, have no fear. Thick calluses do not have to be rough. In fact, keeping them manually trimmed and polished actually helps them grow more healthily and prevents cracking. Much like the split ends that your hair experiences when not maintained, your calluses need frequent trims as well. However, if you are frequently barefoot on rough, rocky, uneven surfaces, the possibility of naturally trimming the sides of your feet -- the part that typically cracks first -- is more likely. By natural trimming, I mean the act of continually being barefoot on rough surfaces. If, on the other hand, you are mostly going barefoot on grass or even pavement, the lack of rocky and uneven surfaces will mean that you are unlikely to scrape the sides of your feet and toes, which would otherwise automatically trim the calluses in these areas. Keeping calluses well maintained actually helps grow them thicker, faster. If you allow the outermost layer to get too dry without sloughing it off, it will be too disconnected from the moisture of the body, will harden, and eventually crack. Since I am proposing an increase in barefoot activities as eustress rather than as an extreme and radical change, you will likely simply need to get a foot scrubber or scraper and give them a good scrubbing three or four times a week. This is also a magnificently efficient way to clean dirty looking feet before bed from a day of barefoot walking.

There is a definite risk/reward benefit in spending time barefoot on natural terrain. Aim to maximize the benefits and minimize the risks. Minimize the chance of foot disease, wounds, burns, bites, injuries, poor hygiene and aesthetics by avoiding public showers and bathroom-type areas while barefoot. Avoid walking barefoot where broken glass or other cutting or poking hazards exist. Wash your feet when you get home and before bed. Carry a pair of sandals or other lightweight shoes in case hazards present themselves unexpectedly while walking barefoot. I am not advocating that you avoid wearing shoes. Instead, slowly increase the amount of time spent barefoot and slowly challenge yourself with the terrain you walk barefoot on. Look after your feet because they have the ability to influence so much of the rest of your body's structure. They are, and should be, the main point of contact between you and the world. Avoid limiting and depriving them of experiencing the nature they evolved to experience. They will reward you for your efforts.

CHAPTER 14

COLD WATER

"Cold water is merciless, but righteous." (Wim Hof)

Cold water therapy is a eustress that is likely the most effective, quickest to administer, and gives you the best results for the time you spend on it. I also think of it as the ultimate non-harmful discomfort. It is one of the most accessible choices to make in an attempt to disrupt the old lack of balance, to take control of your body and mind, and to build your self-confidence in believing that you can truly do anything that you set your mind to.

Just as the cold wolf does not need or ask for a sweater, for the temperature to be turned up, for a fireplace, or a hot water bottle, we humans also do not require these things every minute of every day. Modern-day humans have become lazy in their sedentary lifestyles. They go from their down-filled, duvet-covered beds to their robes, to their hot coffee, to their hot shower, to their warm clothes. Then, they go from their heated houses to their heated cars, to their covered parking spots, to their heated workspaces. They take a break for a heated lunch, return to their heated workspaces, back to their heated cars and to their heated houses to eat their heated dinner. They sit by the fire before tucking themselves into their down-filled duvets, only to repeat the cycle. It sounds very elegant and very comfortable. Maybe too comfortable. And therein lies the problem.

Genghis Khan -- the founder and first Great Khan of the Mongol Empire -- is thought to have noticed the following when he reportedly tried out the saunas and hot tubs of the Chinese cities he sacked: His observation was that the comfort of the warmth made men weak and lazy. He thought that it dulled their senses and made them lose sight of their abilities. After making this observation, he avoided these comforts and slept on his cot in his *ger* (skin-walled yurt) instead.

Today, we tend to associate the luxury of constant warmth with successfully taking care of ourselves, while, in reality and counter-intuitively, we are only weakening our natural strengths and capabilities. The implications of this may not be immediately obvious, but in the long run, many experience health conditions and mental limitations that could have been averted by challenging their bodies a bit more.

Benefits

In the story about John Smith from Chapter 9, we talked about the 14-year-old's accidental resilience to oxygen deprivation. John Smith's survival after being submerged underwater for over 15 minutes is thought to have been due to the fact that the water was freezing cold -- between 32 and 39 degrees Fahrenheit (between 0 and 4 degrees Celsius). In a way, his body was cryogenically preserved. Triggered by this exposure to the cold water, his central nervous system forced the majority of his oxygenated blood away from his extremities to prioritize itself.

A modern-day pioneer has made it his life's passion to explore the effects of cold on the human body. Wim Hof, a Dutch hippie in his youth, practiced, learned, and researched self-control via breathing and cold water therapy. He progressively built up his time in cold water. Even during winter in the Netherlands, he would break the ice in his local canal in order to get in. Over time, he built up his tolerance to over 1 hour and 52 minutes to set a Guinness World Record on May 7, 2018.

This record has been beaten since then. The current record, as of writing this, was set on March 3, 2022 by Valerjan Romanovski. He set a Guinness World Record for full body contact with ice for 3 hours and 28 seconds.

Prior to Romanovski, on December 19, 2020, Romain Vandendorpe set a record of 2 hours, 35 minutes, and 43 seconds. Like Wim Hof, Vandendorpe's reason for setting his record was to build awareness. His inspiration was the sad passing of four-year-old Wonder Augustine, who died of brain stem cancer. His goal is to use his knowledge as a physiotherapist to explore the powers of cold to advance medical knowledge in the treatment of diseases including cancer. Vandendorpe strongly believes that the cold can treat and even cure patients like little Augustine (Vandendorpe 2022).

Wim Hof has also subjected himself to a barrage of experiments in an attempt to awaken the scientific community's eyes to self-healing using cold therapy. He has helped people develop further interest in cold water therapy and its famous ability to reduce all types of inflammation-based diseases and disorders.

As you expose yourself to cold water, your blood vessels constrict and blood flow is reduced. In addition to reducing swelling and inflammation, this also forces cells to release their excess liquid to minimize their chance of freezing. These expressed liquids will also contain cell waste products like lactic acid and other metabolic byproducts.

Years ago, the Red Cross's first aid acronym for remembering how to treat an injured person was RICE (rest, ice, compression, elevation). The "ice" part of that acronym usually involved a bag of peas, locally applied ice cubes, or the like. Of course, wonderful companies like Aircast, Breg, and Nice have come up with inventions that move cold water to reduce inflammation post-injury or post-surgery, but that was about the extent of it. The correct intentions were there, but the comfort zones were not pushed to full-body immersion until heroes like Wim made themselves known.

It is not just the cold that is of importance though. Every cold exposure in these cases -- whether local or fully immersed -- needs to be followed by a warming-up phase. That does not mean jumping into a hot tub after exposure to cold. In fact, that is precisely what I do NOT want you to do.

While the cold exposure makes your body squeeze out its cells to rid them of their excess water and waste products, a warm phase draws fresh blood flow to the cells. Along with the fresh blood comes a fresh supply of hydration and nutrients. Therefore, parts of the body that do not get great blood flow, such as tendons, ligaments, and less used or stagnant body parts, are stimulated to circulate and increase blood flow.

You do not have to go to the extreme of almost drowning or setting a new world record. However, I hope you can now understand that the discomfort of being cold has great potential if applied in a controlled and safe way.

Eustress #8 - Cold water exposure for 2 minutes daily

As the name suggests, cold water exposure or immersion is the act of immersing yourself in cold water for a relatively short period of time. It is a simple yet powerful tool that can help improve your health and well-being in no small measure.

Most people believe that they cannot handle cold exposure but the fact is that they are just adverse to being uncomfortable. It will feel harsh, uninviting, and will torment you from your skin to your core. However, this is not distress. The cold that jolts through the body is a discomfort that, admittedly, does not get much better with practice, but you do build up your confidence by doing it more often. That confidence -- knowing that you are not doing your body any harm and discovering the limitless benefits for your efforts -- will help you with your willpower to continue applying this eustress every day. I like to believe that the deeper the cold penetrates, the deeper the healing effects will go through the body.

Put simply: find a way to immerse yourself in the coldest water that you have access to for a minimum of two minutes per day. This can be used in combination with the added eustresses of movement (Chapter 7), breathing (Chapter 9), massage (Chapter 11), cupping (Chapter 12), and walking barefoot (Chapter 13). After exercise, massage, cupping, and walking barefoot, your body's cells will have waste products to release. This cold water exposure will help squeeze them out, releasing the waste into the bloodstream for your kidneys, liver, and spleen to filter. Deep inhalations and smooth, controlled exhalations will assist in calming you, helping you avoid hyperventilation, and ensuring that you have fresh and adequate oxygenated blood to replenish your body's cells with.

Few things are as invigorating, refreshing, and all-round awesome as a fully-immersed cold water experience. Unfortunately, many people will never experience it because they are afraid of the cold. Either that or they believe that a polar bear dip once a year, at best, is sufficient. If you are one of those people, I challenge you to face your fear and learn how to overcome the self-imposed limitations that you have prematurely imposed upon yourself. Once a year is nowhere near the regular eustress exposure you should be aiming for.

You might want to aim for 15 or more minutes in truly freezing-cold water as an eventual goal. That is a great goal if done safely. However, it may not be reasonable for a busy person. Although building safely to that duration of exposure is undoubtedly beneficial for your body, the time commitment to safely warm yourself up afterward without the use of external heat sources can be challenging enough that you will be less likely to do it regularly. If you apply this cold-water eustress methodically and safely, there should be no need for the use of external methods of heating to warm you up post-cold exposure.

Wim Hof believes that regular exposure to being fully immersed in sufficiently cold water for just two minutes will train the body to destress, activate, optimize muscle tone, and relax. In those two minutes, your vascular system is optimized. Two minutes is all you need. Longer than two minutes is beneficial as well, but that is more for mental training (Hof 2021).

Temperature

Ideally, aim for a water temperature of 45 degrees Fahrenheit (7 degrees Celsius) or colder. The working theory is that the warmer the water is above this temperature, the longer you will need to stay to gain equivalent benefits. In addition, this is not a linear relationship. Warmer than 50 degrees Fahrenheit (10 degrees Celsius) is likely a little too comfortable to be considered eustress. Your cold water exposure should be challenging. If you live near a creek, river, lake, or ocean that has year-round temperatures below 45 degrees Fahrenheit (7 degrees Celsius), then you are in luck and cold water eustress will be easier for you. If such bodies of cold water are only available to you for part of the year, then you are partially lucky. Do not avoid cold water eustress just because it is winter time. That is prime time.

Please be smart about it though. If you need to break the ice in a natural body of water in order to gain access to the underlying cold water, there is an obvious risk that there might be a current underneath that can sweep you away. This could happen while approaching your intended entry point if you are walking over the ice (which may break unexpectedly), or by losing your grip at the hole. It is best to avoid ice holes like these. Rather than expose yourself to a risk like this, an indoor cold water shower will suffice. The risk alone of exposing yourself to possible drowning or hypothermia -- let alone actually drowning or experiencing hypothermia – are examples of distress. We want eustress, not distress.

Those of you who live in too warm a climate or are not near natural water that is deep enough to at least lie down in will have to find a substitute. Here are a couple of ideas.

Cold shower: Subterranean cold water pipes are built underground to prevent them from freezing in winter. This also has the effect of keeping the water from getting too warm in the summer months. Take a thermometer and check the coldest temperature you can get to see if it is sufficient. However, even if you live in a region where cold water pipes do stay cold enough in the summer, you might have temperature control valves behind your shower faucets. These typically prevent you from scalding yourself by mixing the hot and cold water to regulate the temperature. However, this can work against you by not allowing the water to flow 100 percent cold.

Ice bath: Wim Hof has been known to keep a deep freezer outside his house for summer use. He keeps this filled with water, which does not seem to freeze more than a thin layer on top. He unplugs the freezer and breaks the ice before getting in. I cannot speak for the efficacy of using a freezer in this way. It might be too hard on the cooling system of the freezer to endure more than a season at best. However, filling it with ice cube trays that you fill a tub with every day should work wonderfully. To do this, fill a bathtub with the coldest water you have access to. Then, add at least three or four bags full of ice. You can determine how much to add using a thermometer. Once you are under 45 degrees Fahrenheit (7 degrees Celsius), you are good to go. Colder is better. Please realize that you will not be able to get water below 32 degrees Fahrenheit (0 degrees Celsius) without a supercooling device or very specific (and rare) conditions. So do not worry about it being too cold. There is no such thing when it comes to your bathtub, shower, local creek, river, lake, or ocean.

Tips

Here are a few tips to help you overcome your cold aversion:

Start slowly: Do not simply jump into a cold pool, ocean, river, or lake. In fact, I would recommend that, for the first week or two, you avoid even getting your head wet. Wear a warm hat if that helps. Slowly acclimatize yourself to the cold water. By that I do not mean for you to lower the temperature day by day -- I believe that you could start in water as cold as that which Wim Hof used, if it was available. By acclimatize, I mean that you walk in slowly, but not too slowly. Taking 30 seconds to fully submerge yourself from feet to neck should be about right.

Breathe deeply: The breathing exercise from Chapter 9 will really come in handy here. My ideal method is to inhale for three counts at the edge of the water. As I exhale for a count of five, I walk in slowly. At the end of my exhale-5, I stop walking for another inhale-3. Then, I walk again for another exhale-5. My aim is to be submerged up to and including my neck in less than 30 seconds.

Do not accessorize: You should not use a wet suit -- just a simple bathing suit, swim trunks, or a bikini at most. You should not use gloves of any kind. Similarly, you should not use neoprene boots or the like. You want your feet and hands to be cold. They are your furthest extremities. If you attempt to keep them warm with boots or gloves, your warm blood will have to pump through your exposed arms and legs to get the blood there. The goal is to focus the warmth, circulation, and energy to your core and central nervous system. If you have access to a river, lake, or the ocean, it is a wonderful opportunity to incorporate the notes from Chapter 13 on increasing your barefoot time. If you absolutely must protect the soles of your feet from glass, urchins, or other hazards, then aim for a shoe that allows water to flow through it, like a Teva sandal.

Hands down: Keep your hands low, at or below your waist level. Getting the hands and feet cold sooner tends to help get the initial shock over with more quickly.

Be prepared: Make sure you have everything you might need before getting into the water to reduce any possible anxiety while you are in. The list includes something to dry off with like a towel, a dry change of clothes, a hat, a jacket, socks, and shoes.

Cold shower daily: For those who do not easily have daily access to a natural water source but have sufficiently cold water at home, daily cold showers will work wonderfully. Having a two-minute cold shower daily will be more effective than having one 15-minute cold shower of the same temperature once per week. Avoid ending on warm/hot. If you must have a warm/hot shower, do that before the cold shower. End the shower with two or more minutes of cold water. The next best step might be to start cold for two minutes, switch to warm/hot, and then end with cold for two or more minutes. The best yet (as far as cold showers go) would be not to use warm/hot water at all.

Avoid shivering: That is correct. The goal is to avoid shivering throughout this process. Deep breathing should be sufficient to achieve this, although engaging your core is a necessity for many. For those of you who have never heard of or learned how to engage your core, here are some ways that others have attempted to share how they learned to engage their core. It is not an easy thing to explain. Try all these and any other exercises you have heard of or can think of to find what works best for you. Core engaging exercises and metaphors include: Kegel exercises, flexing as if you are holding in the urge to urinate, flexing as you would to hold in the urge to defecate, pretending that you are holding a penny between your butt cheeks and preventing it from falling, or flexing as if somebody is about to punch you in the lower stomach. I believe it to be a combination of almost all of these at first. Eventually you may find what you can relax while maintaining just the engaged core. If you find yourself starting to shiver, consider why this could be happening. If you did not hyperventilate, if you were breathing deeply the entire time and did not yell, and if you were engaging your core the entire time but still ended up shivering, then you likely stayed in too long. It is time to calmly exit the water, dry off, and change out of your wet clothes.

Warm yourself from within: Visualize yourself enjoying the cold water. Picture the sensation of icy water on your skin and the feeling of the refreshing and self-created warmth that you will learn to create for yourself afterwards. After exiting the water, drying off, and changing into dry clothes, you need to learn to warm yourself up from the inside out. This is an excellent time to incorporate the movement and exercises from Chapter 7. In addition to engaging your core, consider squatting down low with your upper legs parallel to the ground and throwing punches. Alternatively, fake a full-body shiver where you start with your hips. Include your shoulders while relaxing your arms and slightly bending your knees. If you do this for about 60 seconds, you will most likely feel quite warm. More typical calisthenics exercises can also be used such as chin/pull ups, push-ups, planks, handstands, burpees, and any similar activities. Just be careful not to do any exercises that are hard on your ligaments or tendons as they might be fragile while cold. For example, I do not recommend going for a run after cold water exposure. Perhaps running on the spot or jumping jacks would be okay, but only if you take care not to cause distress to your cold tendons and ligaments.

Do not use external heat sources: Unless you have started shivering and are unable to get control of it, you should avoid the use any form of external heat source. That means no pre-warmed clothes from a dryer or fire, no hot water bottles, no fireplaces, no saunas, no steam rooms, no warm baths, no warm tubs, no warm showers, no electric blankets, no car heaters. Your warmth should come from within. Try to avoid external heat sources for at least one hour after cold water exposure.

Head dunking: While there is no need to dunk your head under the cold water, if you can make it to two minutes in cold water, do consider it. Even just splashing cold water on your face while the rest of your body is fully immersed will stimulate the vagus nerve. The head does lose a considerable amount of heat. When wet, it will lose heat even faster. If you choose to submerge your head, realize that the idea is to breathe out continually throughout the process. Take a deep, 3-count inhale. Then, slowly exhale as you calmly dunk your head under, still exhaling while submerged and still exhaling the same breath while returning above the surface. You can see how practicing the Inhale-3, Exhale-5 breath cycle from Chapter 9 can come in handy here. The reason for the constant exhale while submerged -- versus a breath hold -- is to ensure that you are not tempted to hyperventilate. If you lack the ability to control your breathing while dunking your head, then you are not yet ready to do it. Be patient and kind with your body. Also, be aware that, with head dunking, there is a chance of giving yourself a bit of a brain freeze -- also known as ice cream headache. These are annoying, but do go away fairly quickly, just like with ice cream. However, it is a good indication that you have stayed under too long -- even if you only submerged your head for a few seconds. Do not try to stay submerged longer than you are ready for and remind yourself that you do not even have to submerge your head for the eustress benefits. The extreme of diving into cold water head-first is never a good or safe idea. It is most certainly not a controlled example of eustress.

Sleep: You will likely find that exposure to sufficiently cold water -- even for just two minutes -- will make your body work so hard to rewarm itself that you will either feel the need for a midday nap or the desire to go to bed early that night. By all means listen to your body.

Counterintuitive: There is another counterintuitive benefit that makes cold water exposure a little bit addictive after a while. When you leave a hot shower or hot tub on a cold day, you are almost always cold when you get out, regardless of what you do next, because the air out of the water is cooler than the water temperature was. However, once you are used to ending with a two-minute (or longer) cold shower or bath, you will only feel warmer when you step out because the air temperature will be warmer than the cold water was. This feeling is the same when leaving a cold ocean, lake, stream, or river.

The pain of the cold will pass -- typically after about two minutes. Once it does, you will grow to believe that it is a mental pain. Your body is fine. Your body is better than fine. It is relearning how to heal itself. If you can convince yourself to endure just two minutes per day of sufficiently cold water, you can truly do anything that you set your mind to.

Additional or alternatives

Here are additional ideas that have nothing to do with cold water, yet can be effective as well.

Feet up: If you live in a hot desert, have no access to cold water, or have no electricity to cool the water that you do have access to, this will at least help your leg circulation if done a minimum of three or four times per week. However, it offers just a limited and partial benefit when compared with cold water exposure. Lie on your back with your hips propped up by a thick pillow and your feet straight up in the air against a wall. If your hips are raised above the level of your heart, this position will allow the blood in your legs and hips to drain more than if you were simply to lie down flat. If you hold this position for a minimum of 15 minutes per session, three to four times per week, you will be simulating a small part of what cold water exposure to your lower body would do. If you are doing this in place of cold water exposure you will miss out on many immune system benefits and neurotransmitter releases that your body will be unlikely to trigger without the cold water eustress. However, you may relieve leg inflammation and other potential lower body circulatory problems over time. You will find that your feet will feel very cold due to the decreased blood flow. This is normal. Just be sure that you do not lose sensation in your feet. If you do, check that you are not causing distress to your back with the pillow that is raising your hips.

If it is too difficult for you to raise your legs up against a wall, an alternative is to have your lower legs on a sofa or bed. You will still be on your back, on the floor, and with your hips raised above the level of your heart.

If you are looking for more of a challenge, consider headstands or handstands. However, being able to do a head- or handstand for a minimum of 15 minutes is fairly difficult. Be kind and patient with your body.

Save money, the environment, and improve health: In general, quite apart from using the eustress of cold water exposure, unless you are ill, you should avoid taking a hot shower, using a hot tub, a hot water bottle, an electric blanket, a sauna, or a steam room, avoid turning up the thermostat, as well as avoid other artificial body-warming devices for the purpose of warming up when you are cold. I would go so far as to advocate avoiding extra sweaters, jackets, and hats if you are inside or if the weather does not require it. In fact, I recommend that you turn down your home thermostat in the winter by a few degrees, ESPECIALLY if you are feeling cold. I know it sounds counter intuitive. These devices are all wonderful tools to use when really necessary, but when you are just feeling cold due to a lack of activity, avoid them.

Consider that you feel cold because you are not active enough at that point in time for the environment that you are in, the age you are at, and the condition that you are in. Instead, consider warming yourself up before reaching for external aids Refer to the exercises in Chapter 6 and Chapter 7 to achieve this. If you have adequately warmed yourself up by deep breathing and exercise and are not cold again after about an hour, then you can reward yourself with a body-warming device if you still feel that you want it.

Reducing your house thermostat in the winter will help you have less of an impact on the environment and save you money on heat, electricity, and gas at the same time. The icing on the cake is that you will be helping your own body's health at the same time.

CHAPTER 15

MUSIC

"What worries you, masters you." (John Locke)

Even though the American Music Therapy Association agrees that the use of music can improve physical, mental, and emotional well-being and can also be used to help with conditions such as anxiety, depression, Alzheimer's disease, and more (Novotney 2013), my inclusion of music here is for a different yet specific purpose.

Too many people stop playing musical instruments or singing regularly after high school -- sometimes sooner. The mental eustress of learning a new scale, developing a different embouchure (facial muscles needed to play an instrument), memorizing a tough section, trying to be in tune, and relaxing enough to improvise can be combined harmoniously with the breathing theory in Chapter 9. In that Chapter 9, you worked up to an Inhale-3, Hold(full)-1, Exhale-5, Hold(empty)-4. In the case of music, the counts are based on the rhythm and music stanzas rather than on counting heartbeats, Mississippis, or Live-Love-Laugh-Learns.

The requirement to pay full attention to notes, rhythm, words, pitch, and tone does not allow the mind to wander very much.

"What worries you, masters you." Most people have a hard time having worries on their mind while they are trying to focus on notes or words and making happy, lively music. This is leagues different from just listening to music.

Music therapists can use both active and passive music experiences to achieve client goals. Active music experiences may require you to try songwriting, playing instruments, and moving to music, while passive experiences mostly involve listening.

Eustress #9: Become musical daily

Of course, there are benefits to passive music experiences. There are also great benefits to playing percussion and string instruments. However, these activities and instruments do not support the advice from Chapter 9 on breathing.

Any time you have to inhale deeply and quickly followed by a slow and controlled exhale, you are repeating our breathing exercises in a different form. The added benefit here is the assistance of music to help you focus. This eustress is absolutely perfect for people who might consider themselves tone-deaf, those who have never played an instrument, cannot read music, or otherwise do not consider themselves to be musically inclined. They are typically the ones who have been limiting their inner musician and need it the most.

I am challenging you to find and incorporate music as eustress to support improved breathing habits.

Instruments

For the purpose of eustress and breathing, avoid creating music with anything that does not directly require your diaphragm to move air in order to make the sound. That leaves many choices, such as brass or woodwind instruments, as well as all other wind aerophone instruments (like the didgeridoo), to name a few. However, please note that the harmonica is not ideal for our current purpose as it produces sound on the inhale as well. However, singing is absolutely included. Just be sure that your inhales are always through your nose. This makes it considerably harder -- but eustress *should* be a challenge.

To be clear, there is nothing wrong with playing other instruments. My intention here is to generate a will to play a new instrument, to revive an old one, or to learn one that you have always wanted to play that simultaneously encourages you to improve your breathing, and to integrate it into your regular repertoire.

Tips

Cost: If you are not sure what instrument you should use that will be suitable, or if you want to try several to help you choose, consider your local music store. They typically rent a wide variety of instruments for a week or month. Make a list of the instruments you would like to try and go through them all before making a decision. Then look for used ones. You need to play, not to perform or play well. The goal is to move air. You do not need professional quality, new instruments for this purpose. In fact, you do not need an instrument at all if cost is an issue and you enjoy singing.

Circular breathing: An added challenge is to attempt circular breathing. This is a specific technique where you inhale through the nose while simultaneously pushing air through your lips using your cheeks. The inhaled breath is then merged to refill the cheeks in order to repeat it, thereby maintain a constant exhalation. This typically works best on lower airflow instruments, but it can be used on any instrument. It is commonly used with the trumpet, French horn, flute, oboe, and didgeridoo, to name a few. You can try it out now to get a taste of it.

First, fill your mouth with air so that your cheeks are puffed out and hold it in there. Then, inhale deeply through your nose while maintaining the air in your mouth. Now, let a small, steady stream of air through your lips. When you feel that your mouth has about half of its air capacity left, replenish it by exhaling gently through your mouth. This is done without letting more than a small, steady stream of air through your lips throughout the change from the air in your cheeks to the exhale from your lungs. ALlow your exhale to fill your cheeks faster than the air is leaving your lips. Once your cheeks are full again, maintain the pressure of the steady stream through your lips using only your cheeks as you inhale and repeat the cycle.

The challenge is to appear to exhale continuously by creating a sound in an instrument without listeners hearing that you inhaled.

Singing: Singing is one of the most affordable methods of this breathing process. I would only encourage you to sing loudly rather than just lightly under your breath. It is not much of a challenge to sing in a whisper. Projecting more sound requires a more forceful and steady exhale. A more forceful and steady exhale requires an increased lung capacity. Inhaling more air for that increased lung capacity requires a stronger diaphragm.

Whistling: Whistling is as wonderful as singing. The only problem with it is that it does not tend to challenge you to take deeper breaths. From a breath-count perspective, singing Happy Birthday loudly is much more difficult than whistling it at the same speed.

Humming: One of the downfalls of playing instruments and singing for the purpose of musical eustress is that they all require exhaling through the mouth. Humming, on the other hand, can be accomplished with both inhaling and exhaling through your nose.

Luftpause: The "luftpause" in written music is the apostrophe-like mark that indicates that you may inhale. It is also known as a breath mark. These are rarely mid-verse or mid-sentence. Be sure to pay attention to these and aim to inhale when you either see or hear them. This will help you inhale deeply and not exhale too quickly.

Rests: The "rests" in music refer to the musical pauses between playing, singing, whistling, or humming. When performing along with music, avoid taking breaks at the rests or pauses between played, sung, whistled, or hummed tones. Instead, hold the last note as long as possible. Again, the object is quick, deep inhales followed by long and controlled exhales that are tied to rhythm and stanzas.

Dance: Dance on its own is a great movement exercise. Consider applying it while playing, singing, whistling, or humming. That will require that your body coordinates muscle movements with a jingle and coordinated breaths. Even if you are just humming through your nose while actively dancing (paying attention to the *luftpause*), you will be challenging yourself in a brilliant way. This might look like humming and dancing ballet or a jig, playing a trumpet while marching, singing along with your favorite singer's choreographed music video, or anything else that requires you to control your breath while moving actively.

You do not need to perform, share, sing, whistle, hum, or dance to your music with or for anybody if you choose not to. This is all about quick, deep inhales followed by slow, controlled, long exhales. However, frequently practicing with pride and intent can do wonders for your self-confidence and makes a wonderful goal along your path to *Fixing Yourself*.

CHAPTER 16

CONCLUSION

"I'm not afraid to die. But I'm afraid to not live."
(Wim Hof)

To LIVE well, we all need to keep striving to better ourselves. Naming your unwanted habits is a first step in the right direction. Research within yourself and acknowledge what triggers the unwanted habits that you choose to uncover. Every unwanted habit has a matching perceived limitation. Oftentimes these limitations are just that -- perceived. There might be an element of fear or simply a memory that causes you to believe that you are limited.

Being able to choose new, healthier responses to your unwanted habit triggers and forcing yourself to make new habits in their place is easier said than done. The same applies to breaking through a perceived limitation. Willpower will help, but confidence to support your willpower and the desire to change for the better will ultimately be your savior.

To help you build your confidence, I have presented you with nine eustress activities for you to implement. I recommend that you do all of them. They are all beneficial, reasonable, possible to start immediately, and do not cost much -- if anything --

other than your time. These eustresses have the added benefit of triggering hidden mammalian powers that you were born with yet either forgot that you had or have never even used before. Your body is on your side to help you use purposeful and beneficial eustress to train yourself to naturally become free from your perceived limitations.

If the cost required is just time and effort and the risk involved is low to none, it should be a no-brainer to test these theories on yourself. Yes, you might exercise a little more, eat, breathe, drink, and treat yourself a little differently and more mindfully. The real risk is that you might get too excited and push too fast, too hard, too soon -- not listening to your body. You might temporarily be tired, hungry, out of breath, thirsty, sore, cold, or less comfortable than you normally would have been. But these are all necessary to receive the benefits that accompany eustress.

Although the human body is amazing and exceedingly resilient, you still need to be gentle to and forgiving with yours. Consider attempting to make up for a lifetime of neglecting your body by starting immediately.

All of these eustress activities should cause you some discomfort, require willpower, and require repetition. This is eustress -- the healthy stress -- to help you to *Fix Yourself*.

This is the first of a tetralogy -- a four-book series -- focused on helping you realize that, if you are not "Living, Loving, Laughing, or Learning" to the best of your abilities at any point in time, then something is amiss.

I wish you godspeed in your journey to *Fix Yourself and LIVE the Happy Path by using 9 Eustress Exercises to Transform, Change Habits, and Find Balance.*

"Yesterday is gone. Tomorrow has not yet come.
We have only today. Let us begin."
(Mother Teresa)

ACKNOWLEDGMENT

I would like to express my deep gratitude to my invaluable Editor, Almiria Wilhelm.
Her kind of patience, guidance, suggestions, and knowledge cannot be underestimated.

AFTERWORD

I hope you have enjoyed reading this book as much as I enjoyed the experiences that led to writing it.
I would be grateful if you could leave a review on Amazon.

If you would like to be notified of future publications in this series, here is a link to sign up and be the first to know:
https://subscribepage.io/JulianCasper

Live the life you ***love***, and ***laugh*** as you ***learn*** to endlessly grow.
– Julian Casper

REFERENCES

- Aboushanab, TS, & AlSanad, S (2018). Cupping Therapy: An Overview from a Modern Medicine Perspective. *Journal of Acupuncture and Meridian Studies, 11*(3), 83–87.

- Al-Bedah, AMN, Elsubai, IS, Qureshi, NA, Aboushanab, TS, Ali, GIM, El-Olemy, AT, Khalil, AAH, Khalil, MKM, & Alqaed, MS (2019). The medical perspective of cupping therapy: Effects and mechanisms of action. *Journal of Traditional and Complementary Medicine, 9*(2), 90–97.

- Aggarwal, I, Wadhawan, M, & Dhir, V (2016). Myobraces: Say No to Traditional Braces. *International Journal of Oral Care and Research, 4*(1), 82–85.

- Angevaren, M, Aufdemkampe, G, Verhaar, HJJ, Aleman, A, & Vanhees, L (2008). Physical activity and enhanced fitness to improve cognitive function in older people without known cognitive impairment. *Cochrane*

Database of Systematic Reviews, 3. https://doi.org//10.1002/14651858.CD005381.pub2. Accessed Dec. 1, 2022.

- Assadi, SN (2017). What are the effects of psychological stress and physical work on blood lipid profiles? *Medicine (Baltimore), 96*(18).
- Bard, P (1934). Emotion: I. The Neuro-humoral Basis of Emotional Reactions. In C. Murchison (Ed.), *A handbook of general experimental psychology* (pp. 264–311). Clark University Press. https://doi.org/10.1037/11374-006. Accessed on Dec. 1, 2022.
- Bucklin, SM (2017, Aug. 11). *What are 'depression naps' and are they a sign of trouble?* Today. https://www.today.com/health/what-are-depression-naps-are-they-sign-trouble-t114981. Accessed on Dec. 1, 2022.
- Burton, J (2010). *WHO Healthy Workplace Framework and Model: Background and Supporting Literature and Practice*. https://apps.who.int/iris/rest/bitstreams/517787/retrieve. Accessed on Dec. 1, 2022.
- CDC (2018). *Summary Health Statistics: National Health Interview Survey, 2018*. https://www.cdc.gov/nchs/fastats/sinuses.htm.

Accessed on Dec. 1, 2022.

- Cleveland Clinic (2020, Nov. 18). *Should I Breathe Through My Mouth or Through My Nose?* https://health.clevelandclinic.org/breathe-mouth-nose. Accessed on Dec. 1, 2022.

- Cleveland Clinic (2020, Dec. 23). *Surprising Facts About Your Nose.* https://health.clevelandclinic.org/7-surprising-facts-nose. Accessed on Dec. 1, 2022.

- Cooper, JS, Phuyal, P, & Shah, N (2022). *Oxygen Toxicity.* StatPearls Publishing. https://www.ncbi.nlm.nih.gov/books/NBK430743. Accessed on Dec. 1, 2022.

- Critchley, HD (2009). Psychophysiology of neural, cognitive and affective integration: fMRI and autonomic indicants. *International Journal of Psychophysiology* *73*(2), 88–94. https://www.sciencedirect.com/science/article/pii/S0167876009001020. Accessed on Dec. 1, 2022.

- da Silva, SG, & Arida, RM (2015). Physical activity and brain development. *Expert Review of Neurotherapeutics*, *15*(9), 1041–51. https://doi.org/10.1586/14737175.2015.1077115. Accessed on Dec. 1, 2022.

- Das, J (2022, May 24). *The Science of Stress.* The Franklin Institute. https://www.fi.edu/blog/science-of-stress. Accessed on Dec. 1, 2022.
- Didari, T, Mozaffari, S, Nikfar, S, & Abdollahi, M (2015). Effectiveness of probiotics in irritable bowel syndrome: Updated systematic review with meta-analysis. *World Journal of Gastroenterology, 21*(10), 3072–84.
- Duhigg, C (2012). *The Power of Habit.* Random House.
- Friedman, M, (2009). *Sleep Apnea and Snoring: Surgical and Non-Surgical Therapy*, 1st ed. Saunders Elsevier.
- Galbo, H (1983). *Hormonal and metabolic adaptation to exercise.* Georg Thieme Verlag.
- Genovese, M (2020). *Eustress: The Good Kind of Stress. Adrenal Fatigue Team.*
- Gibran, K (~1925). https://www.goodreads.com/quotes/32664-your-living-is-determined-not-so-much-by-what-life. Accessed on Dec. 1, 2022.
- Gudden, J, Arias Vasquez, A, & Bloemendaal, M (2021). The Effects of Intermittent Fasting on Brain and Cognitive Function. *Nutrients, 13*(9), 3166.
- Harvold, EP, Tomer, BS, Vargervik, K, & Chierici,

G (1981). Primate experiments on oral respiration. *American Journal of Orthodontics, 79*(4), 359–72.

- Hecht, E, Rabil, A, Steele, EM, Abrams, G, Ware, D, Landy, D, & Hennekens, C (2022). Cross-sectional examination of ultra-processed food consumption and adverse mental health symptoms. *Public Health Nutrition*, *25*(11), 3225–34.

- Hirshkowitz, M, Whiton, K, Albert, SM, Alessi, C, Bruni, O, DonCarlos, L, Hazen, N, Herman, J, Katz, ES, Kheirandish-Gozal, L, Neubauer, DN, O'Donnell, AE, Ohayon, M, Peever, J, Rawding, R, Sachdeva, RC, Setters, B, Vitiello, MV, Ware, JC, & Adams Hillard, PJ (2015). National Sleep Foundation's sleep time duration recommendations: methodology and results summary. *Sleep Health*, *1*(1), 40–43.

- Hof, W (2021). *The Secret Truth About The Iceman* [YouTube video]. https://www.youtube.com/watch?v=tCF_UYqm2w8. Accessed on Dec. 1, 2022.

- Holowka, NB, Wynands, B, Drechsel, TJ, Yegian, AK, Tobolsky, VA, Okutoyi, P, Ojiambo, RM, Haile, RW, Sigei, TK, Zippenfennig, C, Milani, TL, & Lieberman, DE (2019). Foot callus thickness does not trade off protection for tactile sensitivity during walking. *Nature 571*(7764), 261–64.

- Hwangbo, DS, Lee, HY, Abozaid, LS, & Min, KJ (2020). Mechanisms of Lifespan Regulation by Calorie Restriction and Intermittent Fasting in Model Organisms. *Nutrients, 12*(4), 1194. https://doi.org/10.3390/nu12041194. Accessed on Dec. 1, 2022.

- Institute of Medicine of the National Academies (NA) (2011). *Dietary Reference Intakes for Calcium and Vitamin D.* The National Academies Press. https://doi.org/10.17226/13050. Accessed on Dec. 1, 2022.

- Kayser, R (1895). Die exacte Messung der Luftdurchgangigkeit der Nase. In B Frankel (Ed.) *Archich für Laryngologie und Rhinologie*, vol. 3–4 (pp. 101–20). August Hirschwald.

- King, SL, & Hegadoren, KM (2002). Stress Hormones: How Do They Measure Up? *Biological Research For Nursing, 4*(2), 92–103.

- Koch, JD, Miles, DK, Gilley, JA, Yang, CP, & Kernie, SG (2008). Brief Exposure to Hyperoxia Depletes the Glial Progenitor Pool and Impairs Functional Recovery after Hypoxic-Ischemic Brain Injury. *Journal of Cerebral Blood Flow & Metabolism, 28*(7), 1294–306.

- Kwako, LE, & Koob, GF (2017). Neuroclinical Framework for the Role of Stress in Addiction. *Chronic*

Stress (Thousand Oaks), Jan-Dec.

- Lachance, L (2015). Food, Mood, and Brain Health: Implications for the Modern Clinician. *Missouri Medicine, 112*(2), 111–15.

- Leiper, J, & Molla, A (2003). Effects on health of fluid restriction during fasting in Ramadan. *European Journal of Clinical Nutrition, 57*(Suppl. 2), S30–S38.

- Lewis, M (2015). *The Biology of Desire: Why Addiction is Not a Disease.* PublicAffairs.

- Ljungberg, T, Bondza, E, & Lethin, C (2020). Evidence of the Importance of Dietary Habits Regarding Depressive Symptoms and Depression. *International Journal of Environmental Research and Public Health, 17*(5), 1616.

- Lu, Z, Breidt, F, Plengvidhya, V, & Fleming, HP (2003). Bacteriophage ecology in commercial sauerkraut fermentations. *Applied and Environmental Microbiology, 69*(6), 3192–202.

- Lupu, I, & Ruis-Castro, M (2021, Jan 29). *Work-Life Balance Is a Cycle, Not an Achievement.* Harvard Business Review. https://hbr.org/2021/01/work-life-balance-is-a-cycle-not-an-achievement. Accessed on Dec. 1, 2022.

-

Mayo Clinic (2021, June 17). *Exercise intensity: How to measure it.* https://www.mayoclinic.org/healthy-lifestyle/fitness/in-depth/exercise-intensity/art-20046887#:~:text=You%20can%20calculate%20your%20maximum,beat%20per%20minute%20during%20exercise. Accessed on Dec. 1, 2022.

- Mew, JRC (2004). The postural basis of malocclusion: A philosophical overview. *American Journal of Orthodontics and Dentofacial Orthopedics, 126*(6), 729–38.
- National Institutes of Health (NIH) (2022, Oct. 6). *Calcium: Fact Sheet for Health Professionals.* https://ods.od.nih.gov/factsheets/Calcium-HealthProfessional.
- Novotney, A (2013). Music as medicine. *Monitor on Psychology, 44*(10), 46. https://www.apa.org/monitor/2013/11/music. Accessed on Dec. 1, 2022.
- Phillips, MCL (2019). Fasting as a Therapy in Neurological Disease. *Nutrients, 11*(10), 2501.
- Pinhasi, R, Eshed, V, & von Cramon-Taubadel, N (2015). *Malocclusion and dental crowding arose 12,000 years ago with earliest farmers, study shows.* UCD Dublin.

https://www.ucd.ie/news/2015/02FEB15/050215-Malocclusion-and-dental-crowding-arose-12000-years-ago-with-earliest-farmers-study-shows.html. Accessed on Dec. 1, 2022.

- Price, WA (1932). Control of Dental Caries and Some Associated Degenerative Processes Through Reinforcement of the Diet with Special Activators. *The Journal of the American Dental Association, 19*(8), 1339–69.
- Robin, P (1934). Glossoptosis Due to Atresia and Hypotrophy of the Mandible. *American Journal of Diseases of Children, 48*(3).
- Salley, TG (2015). *Sound-Off! An Introduction to the Study of American Military Marching Cadences.* [Master's thesis, University of Massachusetts]. Department of Music and Dance. Thesis. https://scholarworks.umass.edu/cgi/viewcontent.cgi?article=1212&context=masters_theses_2. Accessed on Dec. 1, 2022.
- Schachter, S, & Singer, J (1962). Cognitive, Social, and Physiological Determinants of Emotional State. *Psychological Review, 69*(5), 379–99.
- Selye, H (1975). Stress and distress. *Comprehensive Therapy, 1*(8):9–13.

- Sheehan, CM, Frochen, SE, Walsemann, KM, & Ailshire, JA (2019). Are U.S. adults reporting less sleep?: Findings from sleep duration trends in the National Health Interview Survey, 2004–2017. *Sleep, 42*(2), https://doi.org/10.1093/sleep/zsy221. Accessed on Dec. 1, 2022.

- Shmerling, RH (2020, June 20). *What exactly is cupping?* Harvard Health Publishing. https://www.health.harvard.edu/blog/what-exactly-is-cupping-2016093010402#:~:text=Cupping%20is%20supposed%20to%20draw,worldwide%20have%20been%20adopting%20it. Accessed on Dec. 1, 2020.

- Sinha, R (2008). Chronic Stress, Drug Use, and Vulnerability to Addiction. *Annals of the New York Academy of Sciences, 1141*, 105–30.

- Swayne, M (2013, Mar. 15). *Unhealthy eating can make a bad mood worse.* https://www.psu.edu/news/research/story/unhealthy-eating-can-make-bad-mood-worse. Accessed Dec. 1, 2022.

- Talemal, L (2021). Caloric Intake and its Effect on Aging and Cognitive Slowing: A Review of the Research into Intermittent Fasting. *Journal of Nutritional Medicine and Diet Care, 7*(1), 1–5.

- Trabelsi, K, Rebai, H, El-Abed, K, Stannard, SR,

Khannous, H, Masmoudi, L, Sahnoun, Z, Hakim, A, Fellman, N, & Tabka, Z (2011). Effect of Ramadan Fasting on Body Water Status Markers After a Rugby Sevens Match. *Asian Journal of Sports Medicine, 2*(3), 186–94.

- Trakman, GL, Fehily, S, Basnayake, C, Hamilton, AL, Russell, E, Wilson-O'Brien, A, & Kamm, MA (2021). Diet and gut microbiome in gastrointestinal disease. *Gastroenterology and Hepatology, 37*(2), 237–45.

- Vandendorpe, R (2021). *Les Super Pouvoir du Froid* [YouTube video]. https://www.youtube.com/watch?v=pPtdmppDo64. Accessed on Dec. 1, 2022.

- Wallace, IJ, Koch, E, Holowka, NB, & Lieberman, DE (2018). Heel impact forces during barefoot versus minimally shod walking among Tarahumara subsistence farmers and urban Americans. *Royal Society Open Science*, Mar. 14. https://doi.org/10.1098/rsos.180044. Accessed on Dec. 1, 2022.

- Warden, SJ, Roosa, SMM, Kersh, ME, & Fuchs, RK (2014). Physical activity when young provides lifelong benefits to cortical bone size and strength in men. *The Johns Hopkins University School of Medicine, 111*(14), 5337–42. https://doi.org/10.1073/pnas.1321605111. Accessed on Dec. 1, 2022.

- Weber, B (2022, Jan. 12). *The death of a superstar: How exactly did Michael Jackson die?* Music In Minnesota. https://www.musicinminnesota.com/the-death-of-a-superstar-how-exactly-did-michael-jackson-die/. Accessed on Dec. 1, 2022.

- Wegner, KE, Smyth, JM, Crosby, RD, Wittrock, D, Wonderlich, SA, & Mitchell, JE (2002). An evaluation of the relationship between mood and binge eating in the natural environment using ecological momentary assessment. *International Journal of Eating Disorders, 32*(3), 352–61.

- Yuan, X, Wang, J, Yang, S, Gao, M, Cao, L, Li, X, Hong, D, Tian, S, & Sun, C (2022). Effect of Intermittent Fasting Diet on Glucose and Lipid Metabolism and Insulin Resistance in Patients with Impaired Glucose and Lipid Metabolism: A Systematic Review and Meta-Analysis. International Journal of Endocrinology, Mar 24. https://doi.org/10.1155/2022/6999907. Accessed on Dec. 1, 2022.

ABOUT THE AUTHOR

Julian Casper believes that, at any given point in time, if you are not doing something that improves how you "Live, Love, Laugh, or Learn", then you probably should not be doing it.

Although a huge proponent of travel, home is in the beautiful, energizing, and never-dull mountains of Colorado.
Julian has a wife and two children who he enjoys living, loving, laughing, and learning with.

He is inspired by family, friends, and mentors – both living and fallen – who have instilled in him to seek constant change in the pursuit of living happily as an endless journey.

Printed in Great Britain
by Amazon